Combined
Sound of Living Waters- Fresh Sounds

Combined Sound of Living Waters-Fresh Sounds

Music Edition

compiled by

betty pulkingham
jeanne harper

HODDER AND STOUGHTON
LONDON SYDNEY AUCKLAND TORONTO

ISBN 0 340 23262 5

First published 1978
Sixth impression 1985

Printed in Great Britain for
Hodder and Stoughton Limited,
Mill Road, Dunton Green, Sevenoaks, Kent
by The Thetford Press Limited, Thetford, Norfolk.

Contents

Foreword

We are happy to present a combined music edition of *Sound of Living Waters* and *Fresh Sounds,* a book reflecting the joyous praise, awesome wonder, simplicity and hope which accompany the Holy Spirit's renewal in the Church today. On the whole, the songs included here were chosen because of their proven usefulness in worship. From the coasts of England, the islands of New Zealand, the expansive shores of America these songs roll in like a powerful tide of praise to the Saviour. The ocean is deep and wide; so also is the musical scope of this book. This volume is not limited by period or style, confined to 'youth songs' or content with 'old favourites'. Simply to turn a page may transport you from the measured dignity of Handel to the swinging rock beat of *Godspell.* We believe that both have their place in a mid-twentieth century manual of praise.

Although this is not *just* a collection of music by experts, Vaughan Williams and Bortniansky do have their say. So do a secretary named Sylvia, a young college student, and the four-year-old son of one of the editors! There are songs here which are 'open-ended': verses may be added spontaneously (e.g., '*Thank You, Lord*' and '*I Will Sing*'). Time-honoured words may appear in new musical clothing: one such new hymn setting, 'On Jordan's Bank' was inspired during a choir rehearsal in an English parish Church. Another bright chorus, '*Thank You, Thank You, Jesus*' was transformed into a serene song of worship because ordinary members of an ordinary choir were open to experimentation and willing to expose their tentative ideas to one another. As a result, they truly sang a 'new song' to the Lord.

Finally, this is a songbook for people: for congregations, for prayer groups, for family gatherings. It is not oriented primarily towards solo performances or trained choirs, yet you will find music suitable for both within its pages. (Please note the Choirmaster's Guide.) You will find new musical settings of the Psalms, a large grouping of attractive songs for children, in addition to music for all seasons and for varying uses in worship. It is our hope that this book will in some measure assist your praises and enliven your sense of calling as worshippers. Then indeed our joy would be complete.

Jeanne Harper and Betty Pulkingham
1978

Acknowledgments

The editors are tremendously indebted to Mimi Farra for her gifts of precision and musicianship made available to us unreservedly, and to Edward Prebble and Mary Felton for their loyal administrative and secretarial help. We are grateful to many friends throughout Canada, U.S.A., England and New Zealand, who served as "song resource" personnel in our search for a truly representative selection of songs. Last of all we want to thank the Fisherfolk who have sung, taught, experimented with, improved upon and shared many of these songs throughout the Christian world. For indeed it is through their ministry that many in the Church have come to hear *fresh sounds.*

We regret that for copyright reasons three songs have been deleted from this printing of *Sound of Living Waters.* These are number 31 *All of my life*; 62 *What a great thing it is* and 127 *I am the resurrection.*

Sound of Living Waters

Songs of Renewal

Contents

hallelujah!

songs of praise and thanksgiving

1. Alleluia No. 1

Capo 3 (D)

Don Fishel
Arr. Betty Pulkingham

Rich and broad
Refrain
F(D) Dm(Bm) Gm(Em) C(A)
Al-le - lu - ia, al-le-lu - ia, give thanks to the ris-en Lord. Al-le -
lu - ia, al-le-lu - ia, give praise to his name.
last time
Verses
B♭(G)
1. Je - sus is Lord of all the earth. He is the King of cre - a - tion.
2. Spread the good news o'er all the earth. Je - sus has died and has ris - en.
3. We have been cru - ci - fied with Christ. Now we shall live for ev - er.
Al - le -
name.

4. God has proclaimed the just reward,
   Life for all men, alleluia.

5. Come let us praise the living God,
   Joyfully sing to our Saviour.

2. The canticle of the gift

Capo 2 (Am)

Pat Uhl Howard
Arr. Betty Pulkingham

Joyfully, with a driving rhythm

Refrain

Bm(Am)
A(G)
Bm(Am)
O what a gift! What a won - der - ful gift! Who can

Em(Dm)
Bm(Am)
tell the won - ders of the Lord? Let us

A(G)
Bm(Am)
op - en our eyes, our ears, and our hearts; it is

A(G)
Bm(Am)
Fine
Christ the Lord, it is he!

Bm(Am)
1. In the still - ness of the night when the
2. On the night be - fore he died it was
3. On the hill of Cal - va - ry the
4. Ear - ly on that morn - ing when the
5. Some - day with the saints we will
A(G)
G(F)
A(G)
world was a - sleep, the al - migh - ty word leapt
Pass - ov - er night, and he gath - ered his friends to -
world held its breath, for there for the world to
guards were sleep - ing, back to life came
come be - fore our Fa - ther and then we will shout and dance and
Bm(Am)
out. He came to Ma - ry,
geth - er. He broke the bread,
see, God gave his Son, his
he! He con - quered death,
sing. For in our midst for our
A(G)
G(F)
A(G)
he came to us, Christ came to the land of Gal - i -
he blessed the wine; it was the gift of his love and his
ve - ry own Son for the love of you and
he con - quered sin, but the vic - t'ry he gave to you and
eyes to see will be Christ our Lord and our

Bm(Am)
F♯m(Em)
Bm(Am)
Refrain
- lee.
life.
me.
me!
King.
Christ our Lord and our King!

3. Something in my heart

Lightly and brightly

Anon.
Arr. Betty Pulkingham

E E7 A E

Some - thing in my heart like a stream running free

F♯ B7

makes me feel so hap - py, as hap - py as can be;

E E7 A E

when I think of Je - sus and what he's done for me,

B7
E
some - thing in my heart like a stream run-ning free.

'Something in my heart' may be sung in sequence with the following:

4. Give me oil in my lamp

Anon.
Arr. Betty Pulkingham

Brightly

E
E7
A
1. Give me oil in my lamp, keep me burning. Give me

E
B7
oil in my lamp, I pray. Give me

E
E7
A
oil in my lamp, keep me burning, keep me

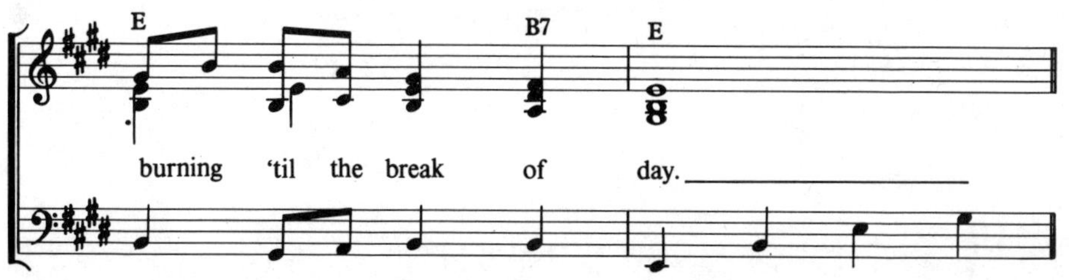
E
B7
E
burning 'til the break of day.

Refrain
E
E7
A
Sing ho - san - na, sing ho - san - na,

B7
1
E
A
E
2
E
sing ho-san-na to the King of Kings! King!

2. Make me a fisher of men, keep me seeking···
3. Give me joy in my heart, keep me singing···
4. Give me love in my heart, keep me serving···

Other verses may be added: Give me faith··· keep me praying; Give me peace··· keep me loving; *etc.*

5. Amazing grace

John Newton

Early American melody
Arr. Betty Pulkingham

Fervently
*G
B7
C
G
G
1. A - ma - zing grace! How sweet the sound that saved a
3. Through ma - ny dan - gers, toils and snares, I have al -

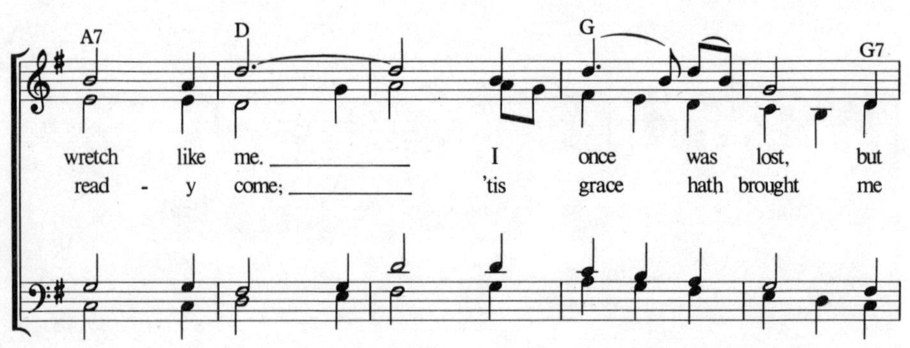

A7
D
G
G7
wretch like me. I once was lost, but
read - y come; 'tis grace hath brought me

C
G
Em
D
G
now am found, was blind, but now I see.
safe thus far, and grace will lead me home.

G
B7
C
G
2. 'Twas grace that taught my heart to fear, and grace my
4. When we've been there ten thou - sand years, bright shin - ing
A7
D
G
G7
fears re - lieved.
How pre - cious did that
as the sun,
we've no less days to
C
G
Em
D
G
grace ap - pear the hour I first be - lieved.
sing God's praise than when we've first be - gun.

* Optional descant for 4th. verse is available by singing the top note in the piano part. Descant in bars 7 and 8 may remain on F sharp.

* Guitar chords are not designed to be used with harmonization of verses 1 and 3.

6. Oh! How good is the Lord

Anon.
Arr. Jeanne Harper

With joyful abandon
Refrain
A
E7
Oh! Oh! Oh! ___ how good is the Lord.
A
Oh! Oh! Oh! ___ how good is the Lord.
A7
D
Oh! Oh! Oh! ___ how good is the Lord. I
A
E7
A
Fine
ne - ver will for - get what he has done for me.

Verses
A
E7
1. He gives me sal – va – tion, how good is the Lord. He
gives me sal – va – tion, how good is the Lord. He
gives me sal – va – tion, how good is the Lord. I
D
ne – ver will for – get what he has done for me.

2. He gives me his blessings ···
3. He gives me his Spirit ···
4. He gives me his healing ···
5. He gives me his glory ···

Other suitable verses may be added: He gives us each other ··· his body ··· his freedom, *etc.*

7. I will sing, I will sing

Max Dyer

Liltingly

I will sing, I will sing a song un - to the Lord. I will
Refrain Al - le - lu, al - le - lu - ia, glo - ry to the Lord. Al - le-
sing, I will sing a song un - to the Lord. I will
lu, al - le - lu - ia, glo - ry to the Lord. Al - le-
sing, I will sing a song un - to the Lord. Al - le-
lu, al - le - lu - ia, glo - ry to the Lord. Al - le-
lu - ia, glo - ry to the Lord.
lu - ia, glo - ry to the Lord.

Optional verses:

We will come, we will come as one before the Lord.
Alleluia, glory to the Lord.

If the Son, if the Son shall make you free,
you shall be free indeed.

They that sow in tears shall reap in joy.
Alleluia, glory to the Lord.

Ev'ry knee shall bow and ev'ry tongue confess
that Jesus Christ is Lord.

In his name, in his name we have the victory.
Alleluia, glory to the Lord.

This song is most effectively sung without any instrumental accompaniment, but with light clapping (finger tips of one hand on palm of another). Suggested rhythm: ♩ ♫♩ ♫♩, etc.

8. Let us give thanks

Brian Howard
Arr. Betty Pulkingham

With driving rhythm, beginning softly and building throughout

Refrain
G
C
G
Let us give thanks
G
C
1G
2G
that our names are writ-ten, writ-ten,
C
G
Am
writ-ten in the book of life, in - scribed up - on his
1G
2G
verse 3
palms. palms.
Fine

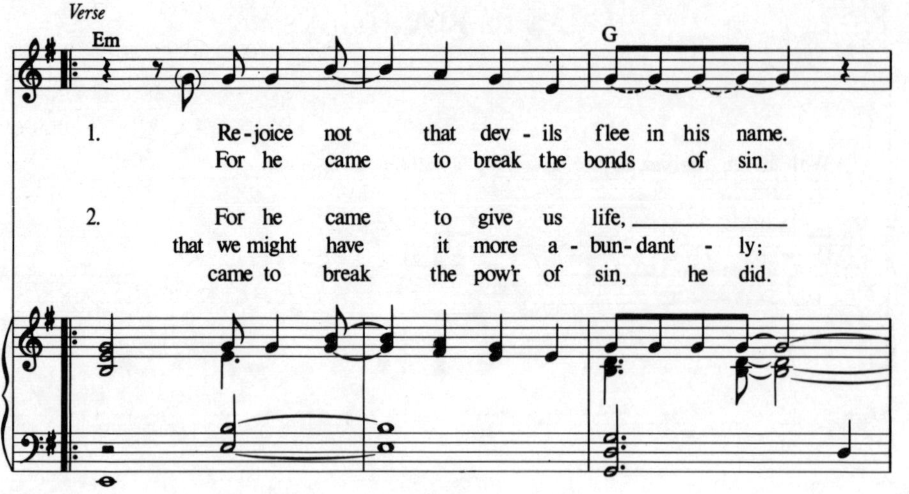
Verse
Em
G
1. Re-joice not that dev-ils flee in his name.
For he came to break the bonds of sin.
2. For he came to give us life,
that we might have it more a-bun-dant-ly;
came to break the pow'r of sin, he did.

no repeat v.1
repeat twice v.2
Em
Re-joice not in the pow-er
Yes, he did, he came to
Yes, he did, he came to

1 G
2 G
that he gave;
set us free, so

Refrain
verse 3 (voices only)
free - ly we sing.
Let ___ us give thanks,

thanks un - to the Fa - ther,

thanks un - to the Son,
thanks to the Ho - ly Spi-

Refrain
- rit,
our Lord God Three in One.

Suggested clapping rhythm:

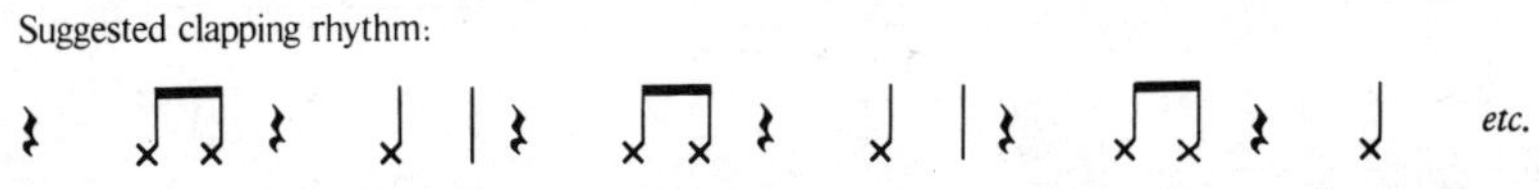
etc.

9. Morning has broken

Eleanor Farjeon

'Bunessan'
Old Gaelic melody
Arr. Betty Pulkingham

With an easy swing (1 beat to a bar)

1. Morn - ing has bro - ken like the first
2. Sweet the rain's new fall, sun - lit from
3. Mine is the sun - light! Mine is the.
morn - ing; Black - bird has spo - ken
heav - en, Like the first dew - fall
morn - ing; Born of the one light
like the first bird. Praise for the
on the first grass. Praise for the
E - den saw play. Praise with e -

sing - ing! Praise for the morn - ing!
sweet - ness of the wet gar - den,
la - tion! Praise ev' ry morn - ing

Praise for them spring - ing fresh from the word.
Sprung in com - plete - ness where his feet pass.
God's re - cre - a - tion of the new day.

10. Rejoice in the Lord always

(2-Part round)

Capo 1 (E)

With a light, happy sound

Anon.

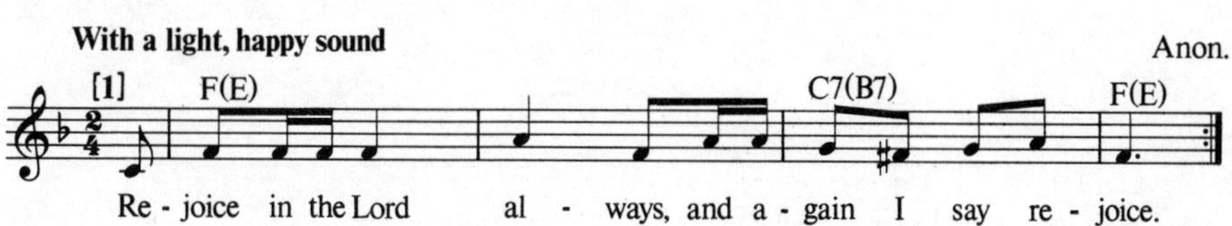
[1]
F(E)
C7(B7)
F(E)
Re - joice in the Lord al - ways, and a - gain I say re - joice.

[2]
F(E)
C7(B7)
F(E)
Re - joice, re - joice, and a - gain I say re - joice.

11. Praise to the Lord

Joachim Neander

'Praise to the Lord'
The Chorale Book for England
Descant by Betty Pulkingham

Joyfully, with dignity

Descant
2. Praise to the Lord, he glo - rious - ly reign - eth; Borne as on ea - gle wings safe - ly sus - tain - eth.
4. Praise to the Lord, O let all a - dore him. All that hath breath join now to a - dore him.
1. Praise to the Lord, the al - might - y, the King of cre - a - tion; O my soul, praise him, for he is thy health and sal - va - tion;
2. Praise to the Lord, o - ver all things he glo - rious - ly reign - eth; Borne as on ea - gle wings, safe - ly his saints he sus - tain - eth.
3. Praise to the Lord, who doth pros - per thy way and de - fend thee; Sure - ly his good - ness and mer - cy shall ev - er at - tend thee;

Hast thou not seen How all thou
Let the a - men sum all our
Join the great throng, Psal - ter - y, or - gan and
Hast thou not seen How all thou need - est hath
Pon - der a - new What the al - might - y can
need - est hath been in what he or - dain - eth.
prais - es a - gain as we wor - ship be - fore him.
song, Sound - ing in glad a - do - ra - tion.
been Gran - ted in what he or - dain - eth?
do, Who with his love doth be - friend thee.

4. Praise to the Lord! O let all that is in me adore him!
All that hath breath join with Abraham's seed to adore him!
Let the 'Amen'
Sum all our praises again
Now as we worship before him.

12. Angel voices ever singing

Francis Pott

'Maiquez'
Geoffrey Beaumont

Smoothly
1. An - gel voi - ces ev - er sing - ing Round thy throne of
2. Thou who art be - yond the far - thest Mor - tal eye can
3. Yes, we know that thou re - joic - est O'er each work of
light, An - gel harps for ev - er ring - ing, Rest not day nor
scan. Can it be that thou re - gard - est Songs of sin - ful
thine; Thou didst ears and hands and voi - ces For thy praise de -
night; Thou-sands on - ly live to bless thee, And con-fess thee
man? Can we know that thou art near us And wilt hear us?
sign; Craftsman's art and mu - sic's mea - sure For thy plea - sure
Lord of might.
Yes, we can.
All com - bine.
1-4
last verse
thee.

From 'Thirty 20th. Century Hymn Tunes'

4. In thy house, great God, we offer
Of thine own to thee;
And for thine acceptance proffer
All unworthily,
Hearts and minds and hands and voices
In our choicest
Psalmody.

5. Honour, glory, might, and merit
Thine shall ever be,
Father, Son and Holy Spirit,
Blessed Trinity.
Of the best that thou hast given
Earth and heaven
Render thee.

13. This is the day

Fiji Island Folk Melody

Cheerfully
1. This is the day, this is the day that the Lord has made, that the
Lord has made. We will re-joice, we will re-joice and be
glad in it, and be glad in it. This is the day that the Lord has made.
We will re-joice and be glad in it.
This is the day that the Lord has made.

2. This is the day when he rose again.
3. This is the day when the Spirit came.

14. Praise him

Anon.

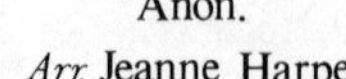
Arr. Jeanne Harper

Smoothly, without dragging

E B7 E E7

1. Praise ___ him, praise ___ him,

A E

praise him in the morn - ing, praise him in the noon - time,

B7 C♯m

praise ___ him, praise ___ him,

E B7 E

praise him when the sun goes down.

2. Jesus ... 3. Love him ... 4. Trust him ... 5. Serve him ...

15. Hallelujah! Jesus is Lord!

Adapted from Rev. 7 Mimi Farra

With rhythmic boldness
A Refrain
G
Hal - le - lu - jah! Hal - le - lu - jah!
A
G
Em
A
Hal - le - lu - jah! Je - sus is (1) Lord!
(2) King!
Verses
D
A
Em A
1. All gath - er round the___ throne of the Lamb,
2. Lift up your voice with the thousands who cry:
3. Bless - ing and hon - or and glo - ry and pow'r
D
A
Em A
his prais - es sing through-out e - ter - ni - ty.
'Wor - thy, wor - thy art thou, Lamb of God.'
be un - to him ______ for - ev - er and ev - er.

4. All glory be to the one Triune God,
, The Father, Son, and the (𝄽) Holy Spirit.

16. Jesus Christ is alive today

Anon.
Arr. Betty Pulkingham

Boldly

A D
Je - sus Christ is a - live to - day, I/we

A E
know I/we know it's true.

A D
Sov' - reign of the U - ni - verse, I/we

A E7 A A7
give him hom - age due.

D
A
Seat - ed there at God's right hand,
B7
E
I am
we are
with him in the pro - mised land.
A
D
Je - sus lives and reigns in
me,
you,
that's
A
E7
A
how I know it's true.

17. O for a thousand tongues

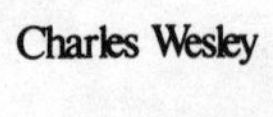
Charles Wesley

'Lyngham'
Thomas Jarman

Joyfully, with movement

1. O for a thou - sand tongues to sing My
2. Je - sus! the name that charms our fears, That
3. He breaks the power of can - celled sin, He

dear re - deem - er's praise, my dear re - deem - er's praise,
bids our sor - rows cease, that bids our sor - rows cease;
sets the pris - oner free, he sets the pris - oner free;

The glo - ries of my God and King, The
'Tis mu - sic in the sin - ner's ears, 'Tis
His blood can make the foul - est clean, His

1. The tri-umphs of his
2. 'Tis life, and health, and
3. His blood a-vailed for

tri - umphs of his grace, The tri - umphs of his
life, and health, and peace, 'Tis life, and health, and
blood a - vailed for me, His blood a - vailed for
grace, The tri - umphs of his grace, The
grace, The tri - umphs of his grace!
peace, 'Tis life, and health, and peace.
me, His blood a - vailed for me.
tri - umphs of his grace, The tri - umphs of his grace!

4. He speaks, and, listening to his voice,
   New life the dead receive,
The mournful, broken hearts rejoice,
   The humble poor believe.

5. Hear him, ye deaf; his praise, ye dumb,
   Your loosened tongues employ;
Ye blind, behold your Saviour come;
   And leap, ye lame, for joy!

6. My gracious master and my God,
   Assist me to proclaim,
And spread through all the earth abroad
   The honours of thy name.

18. Thank you, thank you, Jesus

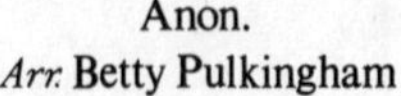

Anon.
Arr. Betty Pulkingham

Cheerfully

E A E

1. Thank you, thank you, Je - sus. Thank you, thank you, Je - sus.

B7

Thank you, thank you, Je - sus, in my heart. ___

E E7 A E

Thank you, thank you, Je - sus. Oh, thank you, thank you, Je - sus.

B7 E

Thank you, thank you, Je - sus, in my heart.

2. You can't make me doubt him. *(repeat)*
You can't make me doubt him in my heart.
You can't make me doubt him,
I know too much about him,
Thank you, thank you, Jesus, in my heart.

3. I can't live without him. *(repeat)*
I can't live without him in my heart.
I can't live without him,
I know too much about him,
Thank you, thank you, Jesus, in my heart.

4. Glory, hallelujah! *(repeat)*
Glory, hallelujah, in my heart!
Glory, hallelujah! *(repeat)*
Thank you, thank you, Jesus, in my heart!

kneel and adore him

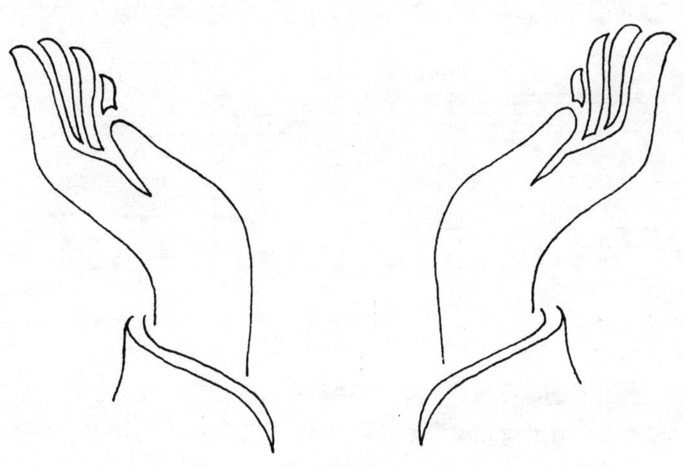

songs of worship

19. Holy, holy

Reverently
Jimmy Owens
C Em/B Dm/A G7 C Em7/B Am7 C/G
melody
(Unison) 1. Ho - ly, ho - ly, ho - ly,
Dm7 G Dm7 G7
ho - ly. Ho - ly, ho - ly, Lord God Al -
C C7 F F/E Dm7 D♯dim7
melody
migh - ty; And we lift our hearts be-fore you as a

C
E
Em7
Am
Dm7
G7
melody
tok - en of our love, Ho - ly, ho - ly, ho - ly,
1-5
C
Dm7
G7
6
C rit.
C
ho - ly. 2. Gra - cious
lu - jah.
rit.

Any of the following may be sung in parts:

2. Gracious Father, gracious Father,
We're so glad to be your children, gracious Father;
And we lift our heads before you as a token of our love,
Gracious Father, gracious Father.

3. Precious Jesus, precious Jesus,
We're so glad that you've redeemed us, precious Jesus,
And we lift our hands before you as a token of our love,
Precious Jesus, precious Jesus.

4. Holy Spirit, Holy Spirit,
Come and fill our hearts anew, Holy Spirit,
And we lift our voice before you as a token of our love,
Holy Spirit, Holy Spirit.

5. Holy, holy, *(same as verse 1)*

6. Hallelujah, hallelujah, hallelujah, hallelujah,
And we lift our hearts before you as a token of our love,
Hallelujah, hallelujah.

20. Let all that is within me

Capo 1(E)

Anon.
Arr. Betty Pulkingham

Freely

F(E) C7(B7)

Let all that is with-in me cry, 'Ho - ly.'

Let all that is with-in me cry,

F(E)

'Ho - ly.' Ho - ly,

B♭(A) F(E) B♭(A) F(E) C7(B7) F(E)

Ho - ly, Ho - ly is the Lamb that was slain.

Let all that is within me cry, 'Worthy'... 'Jesus'... 'glory'

21. Son of God

Oressa Wise

With unhurried simplicity

C G7 C

1. & 4. Son ______ of God, ______ Son ______
2. Word ______ of God, ______ Word ______
3. Lamb ______ of God, ______ Lamb ______

F C F C

______ of God, ______ we come be-fore you to
______ of God, ______ we come to hear you, to
______ of God, ______ we come to bless you, to

G7
C
G7
C
love and a-dore you, Son ______ of God. ______
al - ways be near you, Word ______ of God.
ev - er con-fess you, Lamb ______ of God. ______

22. God himself is with us

Gerhardt Tersteegen

'Tysk'
German melody

Reverently
1. God him - self is with us; Let us all a - dore him,
2. Come, a - bide with - in me; Let my soul, like Ma - ry,
3. Glad - ly we sur - ren - der Earth's de - ceit - ful trea - sures,
And with awe ap - pear be - fore him. God is here with -
Be thine earth - ly sanc - tu - a - ry. Come, in - dwell - ing
Pride of life, and sin - ful plea - sures: Glad - ly, Lord, we
in us: Soul, in si - lence fear him, Hum - bly, fer - vent -
Spi - rit, With trans - fig - ured splen - dor; Love and hon - or
of - fer Thine to be for ev - er, Soul and life and

-ly draw near him. Now his own who have known
will I ren - der. Where I go here be - low,
each en - deav - or. Thou a - lone shalt be known

God, in wor - ship low - ly, Yield their spi - rits whol - ly.
Let me bow be - fore thee, Know thee, and a - dore thee.
Lord of all our be - ing, Life's true way de - cree - ing.

23. # We see the Lord

Isaiah 6:1

Anon.
Arr. Betty Pulkingham

Sung slowly in quiet adoration

E
E
Descant
We see Je - sus.
We see the Lord,

We see Je - sus.
We see the Lord, And he is

B7
E
High, he is high,
high and lift - ed up, And his train fills the tem-ple. He is

B7
E
he is high.
high and lift - ed up, And his train fills the tem - ple. The
A E
A E
An-gels cry, 'Ho ly,' The an - gels cry, 'Ho - ly,' The
an - gels cry, 'Ho - ly,' The an - gels cry, 'Ho - ly,' The
B7
E
A
E
an - gels cry, 'Ho - ly is the Lord.'
an - gels cry, 'Ho - ly is the Lord.'

24. He is Lord

Anon.
Arr. Betty Pulkingham

Broad and full
B7
E
He is Lord, he is Lord. He is
F♯
B7
ris - en from the dead, and he is Lord. Ev' - ry
E
E7
A
F♯m
knee shall bow, ev' - ry tongue con - fess that
E
B7
E
Je - sus Christ is Lord.

25. Alleluia

Anon.
Arr. Betty Pulkingham

With quiet adoration
G C Am
1. Al - le - lu - ia, Al - le - lu - ia, Al - le -
D 1 C G 2 C G
lu - ia, Al - le - lu - ia, Al - le - lu - ia.

2. How I love him 3. Blessed Jesus 4. My Redeemer 5. Jesus is Lord 6. Alleluia

26. Father, we adore you*

(3-part round)

Capo 1 (E)

Terrye Coelho

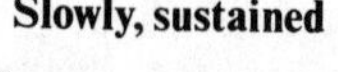
Slowly, sustained

1 F(E) Gm(F#m) C(B7) F(E) 2 Gm(F#m) C(B7) F(E) 3 Gm(F#m) C(B7) F(E)

1. Fa - ther
2. Je - sus
3. Spi - rit

we a - dore you; lay our lives be - fore you. How we love you.

*The original text of this song is 'Father, I adore you; lay my life before you. How I love you.'

27. Thank you, thank you, Jesus

Anon.
Arr. St. Philip's Church, Coventry
Harm. Richard Gullen

Slowly, with deep feeling

E
AM7 E E7
A
1. Thank you, thank you, Je - sus. Thank you, thank you,
F#m G#m
C#m
G#m F#m
Je - sus. Oh, thank you, thank you, Je - sus in my
B7
E
heart. Thank you, thank you,
AM7 E E7
A
F#m G#m
Je - sus. Oh, thank you, thank you, Je - sus. Oh,

C♯m
G♯m
F♯m B7
E
thank you, thank you, Je-sus, in my heart.
1-3
final ending
2. Love you, love you,

2. Love you, love you, Jesus. *(repeat)*
Oh, love you, love you, Jesus, in my heart.

3. Father, God almighty; *(repeat)*
Oh, Father, God almighty, take my heart.

4. Glory hallelujah! *(repeat)*
Oh, glory hallelujah in my heart.

28. Thou art worthy

Rev. 4: 11 and 5: 9, 10.
Verse 2 - Tom Smail

Pauline Michael Mills

Reverently

1. Thou art wor - thy, thou art wor - thy,
2. Thou art wor - thy, thou art wor - thy,
thou art wor - thy, O Lord.
thou art wor - thy, O Lamb.
Thou art wor - thy, to re - ceive glo - ry,
Thou art wor - thy, to re - ceive glo - ry, and
glo - ry and hon - our and power. For
power at the Fa - ther's right hand. For

thou hast cre - a - ted, hast all things cre - a - ted, for
thou hast re - deemed us, hast ran - somed and cleaned us
thou hast cre - a - ted all things.
by thy blood set - ting us free. In
And for thy plea - sure they are cre - a - ted;
white robes arr - ayed us, kings and priests made us, And
thou art wor - thy, O Lord.
we are reign - ing in thee.

29. Spirit of the living God

Capo 3 (D)

Daniel Iverson
Arr. Betty Pulkingham

Unhurried, with a rich sound

(D) (Em) (B7) (Em) (D) (A) (D)
Spi - rit of the liv - ing God, fall a-fresh on me.
(A7) (D) (G) (A7) (D)
Spi - rit of the liv - ing God, fall fresh on me.
(G) (D) (E) (A) (A7)
Break me, melt me, mould me, fill me.
(D) (Em) (B7) (Em) (D) (A7) (D)
Spi - rit of the liv - ing God, fall a-fresh on me.

From SPIRIT OF THE LIVING GOD by Daniel Iverson.

30. Jesus, never have I heard a name

Anon.
Arr. Betty Pulkingham

Tenderly
Je - sus, Je - sus, Je - sus,
1
nev - er have I heard a name that thrills my soul like thine.
2
oh, what match - less grace that links that pre - cious name with mine.

32. Jesus, Jesus, wonderful Lord

Capo 3 (G)

Sylvia Lawton

Tenderly and with warmth

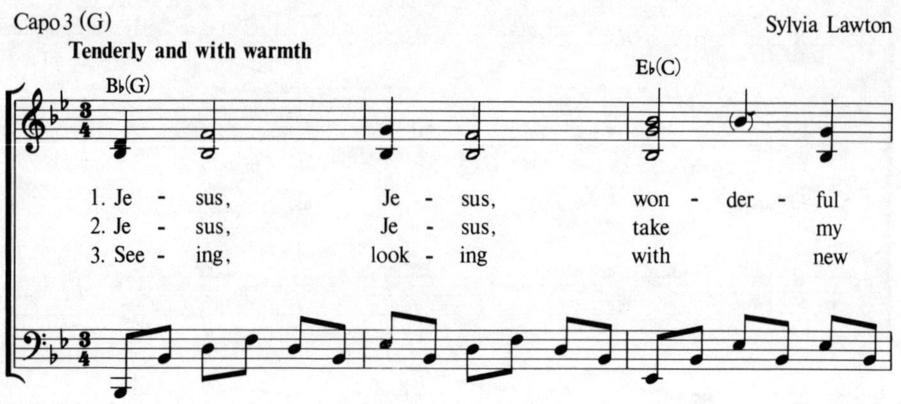

Bb(G)
Eb(C)
1. Je - sus, Je - sus, won - der - ful
2. Je - sus, Je - sus, take my
3. See - ing, look - ing with new

Bb(G)
Lord. Gen - tly you touched me and
life. Je - sus, Je - sus,
eyes; lov - ing, car - ing

Cm(Am)
F7(D7)
Bb(G)
made my life whole; how can I
I give to you, all things,
just as you do; learn - ing

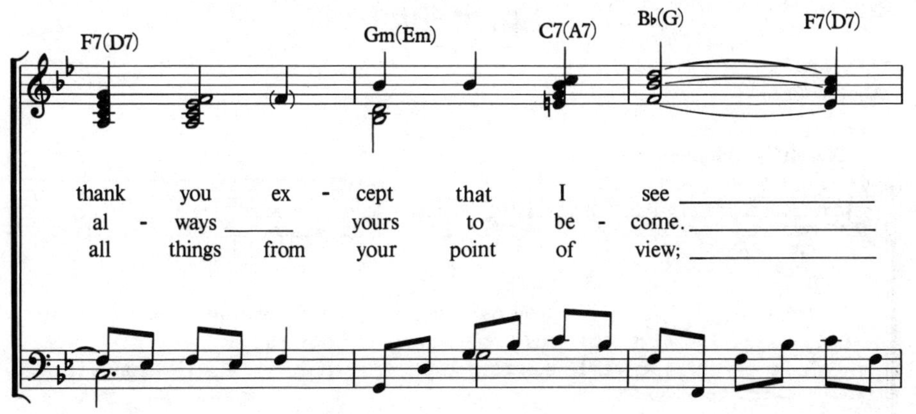
F7(D7)
Gm(Em)
C7(A7)
B♭(G)
F7(D7)
thank you ex - cept that I see
al - ways yours to be - come.
all things from your point of view;

E♭(C)
B♭(G)
F7(D7)
B♭(G)
your way of life is tru - ly for me?
Je - sus my Sav - iour, I will be thine.
Lord Je - sus Christ, your touch is so true.

33. Spirit divine

Andrew Reed

'Graefenberg'
Johann Crueger

Peacefully, with reverence

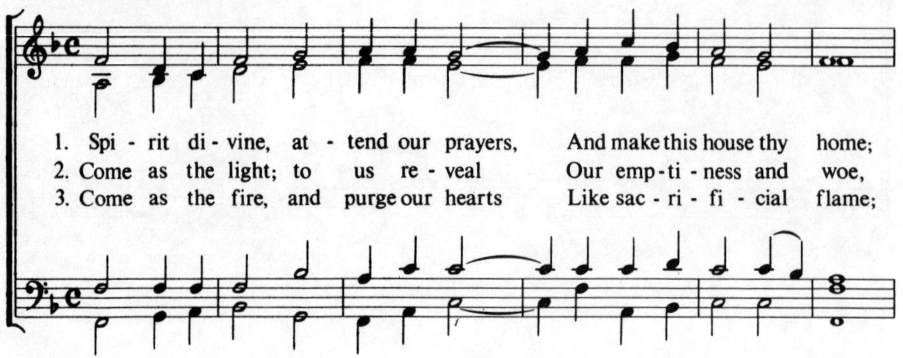
1. Spi - rit di - vine, at - tend our prayers, And make this house thy home;
2. Come as the light; to us re - veal Our emp - ti - ness and woe,
3. Come as the fire, and purge our hearts Like sac - ri - fi - cial flame;

De - scend with all thy gracious powers, O come, great Spi - rit, come!
And lead us in those paths of life Where-on the right - eous go.
Let our whole soul an of-f'ring be To our re - deem - er's name.

4. Come as the dove, and spread thy wings,
   The wings of peaceful love;
   And let thy Church on earth become
   Blest as the Church above.

5. Spirit divine, attend our prayers;
   Make a lost world thy home;
   Descend with all thy gracious powers;
   O come, great Spirit, come!

look up!

songs of hope and vision

34. I want to walk as a child of the light

Kathleen Thomerson

Richly

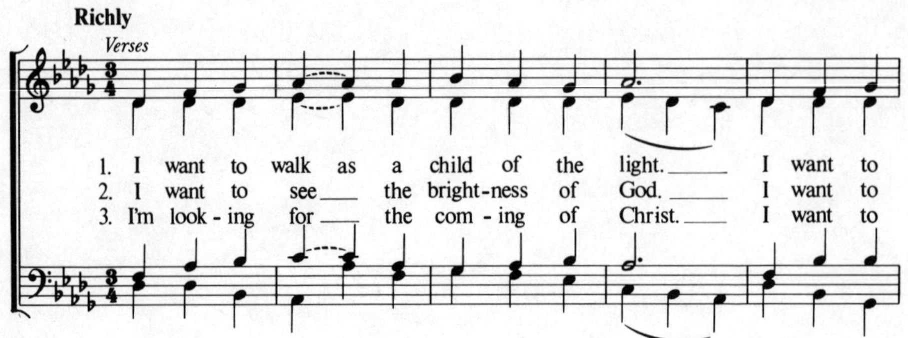

Verses
1. I want to walk as a child of the light. I want to
2. I want to see the bright-ness of God. I want to
3. I'm look-ing for the com-ing of Christ. I want to

fol - low Je - sus. God set the stars to give
look at Je - sus. Clear sun of righteous - ness,
be with Je - sus. When we have run with

light to the world. The star of my life is Je - sus.
shine on my path, and show me the way to the Fa - ther.
pa - tience the race, we shall know the joy of Je - sus.

Refrain
In him there is no dark - ness at all, the

night and the day are both a - like. The

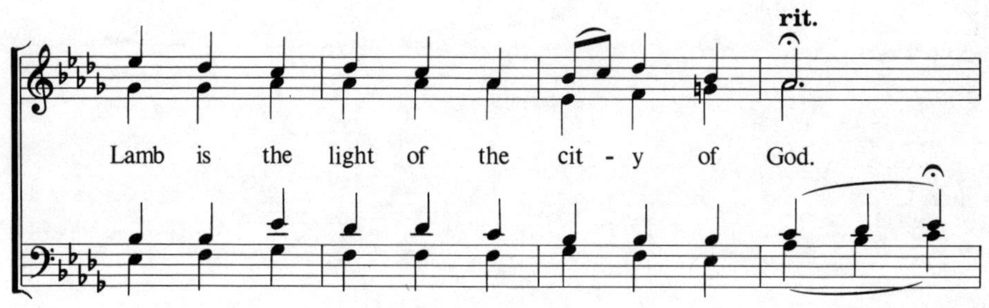
rit.
Lamb is the light of the cit - y of God.

a tempo
Shine in my heart, Lord Je - sus.

35. In Christ there is no east or west

John Oxenham

North American spiritual
Arr. Betty Pulkingham

With breadth
A E G D
1. In Christ there is no east or west, In
2. In him shall true hearts ev - 'ry - where Their
3. Join hands then, broth - ers of the faith, What -
Bm E A D A F#m Bm7
him no south or north, But one great fel - low -
high com - mun - ion find; His ser - vice is the
e'er your race may be; Who serves my Fa - ther
E F#m A E7 A
- ship of love Through-out the whole wide earth.
gold - en cord Close bind - ing all man - kind.
as a son Is sure - ly kin to me.

4. In Christ now meet both east and west,
In him meet south and north.
All Christly souls are one in him
Throughout the whole wide earth.

36. Lord, I want to be a Christian

American folk hymn
Arr. Betty Pulkingham

Thoughtfully, not fast
D
A
D
G
1. Lord, I want to be a Christian, in-a my heart, in-a my
D
A
Bm
G
D
G
heart. Lord, I want to be a Christian in-a my heart, (in-a my
D
G
D
heart,) in-a my heart, (in-a my heart,) in-a my heart, (in-a my
Bm
G
D
heart.) Lord, I want to be a Christian in-a my heart.

2. Lord, I want to be more loving *(etc.)*
3. Lord, I want to be like Jesus *(etc.)*
4. Lord, I want to praise you freely *(etc.)*

37. Day by day

Richard of Chichester
Verse 2 - Jeanne Harper

D. Austin

Gently
F Gm C7 F Dm G7
1. Day by day, dear Lord, of thee three things I
2. Day by day, dear Lord, of thee three things I
C7 F D7 G Gm7
pray: to see thee more clear - ly, to love thee more
pray: to trust thee more full - ly, to leave things more
C C7 F B♭6 F C7 F
dear - ly, to fol - low thee more near - ly day by day.
whol - ly, to lean on thee se - cure - ly day by day.

38.

Day by day

'Godspell'

Stephen Schwartz

Easy waltz feel
FM7
Gm7
FM7
Day by day,
Gm7
FM7
Gm7
Day by day,
B♭M7
Am7
Gm7
O dear Lord, three things I pray:
3
Em7
A7
To see thee more clear - ly,

Em7
A7
Dm
G
love thee more dear - ly,
Fol-low thee more near - ly,

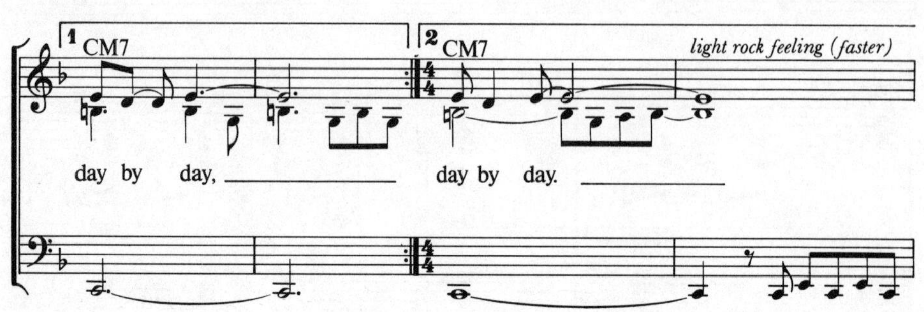
1 CM7
2 CM7
light rock feeling (faster)
day by day,
day by day.

Optional descant
FM7
Gm7
FM7
Day by day,
Day by day,
Day by day,

Gm7
B♭M7
Am7
Day by day,
O dear Lord, three
GM7
Em
Three things I pray
Melody in alto
things I pray,
To see thee more

A
Em
A
Day by day,
Day by day
clear - ly,
Love thee more
dear - ly (Fol - low
Love thee more dear - ly,
dear - ly,
Dm
G
1 CM7
thee.) Fol - low thee more
near - ly,
day by day.

2
CM7
FM7
Day by day,
CM7
FM7
AM7
Day by day by day by day by day by day.

39. Reach out and touch the Lord

Capo 1(E)
Bill Harmon
Simply
F(E)
Bb(A)
F(E)
Reach out and touch the Lord as he goes by. You'll
G(F#)
C7(B7)
find he's not too bus - y to hear your heart's cry. He's
F(E)
Bb(A)
F(E)
pass - ing by this mo - ment your needs to sup - ply. Reach
F6/4(E B bass)
C7(B7)
F(E)
out and touch the Lord as he goes by.

40. I want to live for Jesus every day

Anon.
Arr. Jeanne Harper

Brightly
C
G7
I want to live for Je - sus ev' - ry day. (ev' - ry day)
sim.
C
I want to live for Je - sus, come what may. (come what may)
F
C
A7
Take the world and all its plea - sure, I've got a more en - dur - ing trea - sure.
Dm
G7
C
I want to live for Je - sus ev' - ry day.

2. I'm gonna' live for Jesus ev'ry day *etc.*

41. He shall teach you all things

(for unison voices with optional canon)

Philip Humphreys

Gently, repeat ad lib.
Part 1
Part 2
Piano
He shall teach you all things, He shall teach you all things, and bring all things to your re-mem-brance, and bring all
(mem - brance) He shall teach you all things, He shall teach you all things, and bring all things to your re-mem-brance, and

things to your re - mem - brance.
bring all things to your re -
mem - brance.
rit.
rit.
42.
Kum ba yah
('Come by here')
Traditional Spiritual
Quietly
Kum ba yah, my Lord, Kum ba yah, Kum ba yah, my Lord, Kum ba yah, Kum ba
yah, my Lord, Kum ba yah, O Lord, Kum ba yah.

2 Someone's crying, Lord, Kum ba yah...
3 Someone's singing, Lord, Kum ba yah...
4 Someone's praying, Lord, Kum ba yah...

(Other intercessory verses may be added...Someone's hungry..lonely..wounded..dying, *etc.*)

43. O Breath of Life

Bessie Porter Head

'Spiritus Vitae'
Mary J. Hammond

With sweeping breadth
1. O Breath of Life, come sweep-ing through us, Re - vive thy Church with life and pow'r. O Breath of Life, come, cleanse, re - new us, And fit thy Church to meet this hour.
2. O Wind of God, come, bend us, break us, Till hum - bly we con-fess our need; Then in thy ten - der - ness re - make us, Re - vive, re - store; for this we plead.
3. O Breath of Love, come, breathe with - in us, Re - new - ing thought and will and heart; Come, love of Christ, a - fresh to win us, Re - vive thy Church in ev - 'ry part.

4. Revive us, Lord! Is zeal abating
While harvest fields are vast and white?
Revive us, Lord, the world is waiting,
Equip thy Church to spread the light.

44. Lord of all hopefulness

Capo 1 (D)
Jan Struther

'Slane'
Traditional Irish melody

In unison, with movement
(D) (A7) (D) (D) (A) (Em) (G) (A) (G) (D) (Bm7) (G) (A) (D) (Bm7) (Em) (Em7) (D)
1. Lord of all hope - ful - ness, Lord of all joy, Whose trust, ev - er child - like, no cares could des - troy, Be there at our wa - king, and give us, we pray, Your bliss in our hearts, Lord, at the break of the day.
2. Lord of all ea - ger - ness, Lord of all faith, Whose strong hands were skilled at the plane and the lathe, Be there at our la - bors, and give us, we pray, Your strength in our hearts, Lord, at the noon of the day.
3. Lord of all kind - li - ness, Lord of all grace, Your hands swift to wel - come, your arms to em - brace, Be there at our ho - ming, and give us, we pray, Your love in our hearts, Lord, at the eve of the day.

4. Lord of all gentleness, Lord of all calm,
Whose voice is contentment, whose presence is balm,
Be there at our sleeping, and give us, we pray,
Your peace in our hearts, Lord, at the end of the day.

45. At the name of Jesus

Caroline M. Noel

'King's Weston'
Ralph Vaughan Williams
Descant by
Betty Pulkingham

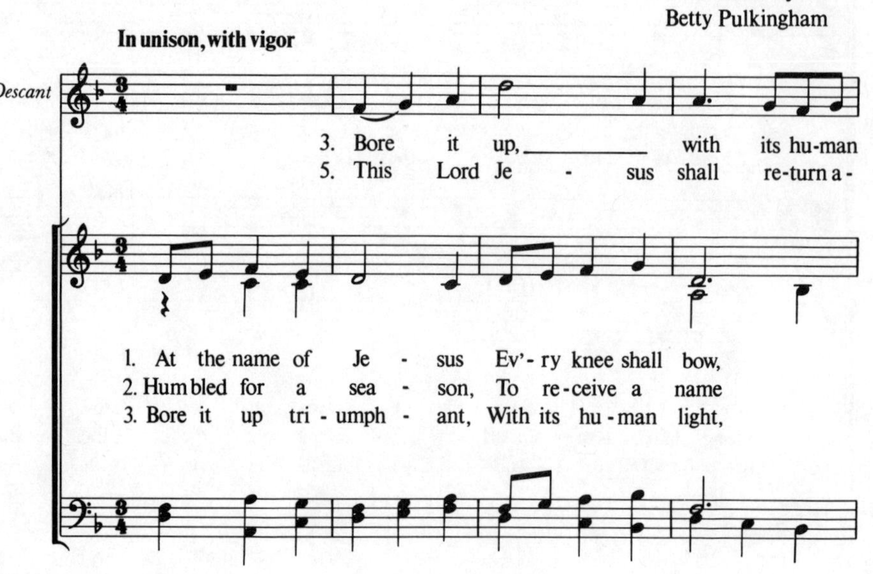

In unison, with vigor
Descant
3. Bore it up, with its hu-man
5. This Lord Je - sus shall re-turn a-
1. At the name of Je - sus Ev'-ry knee shall bow,
2. Humbled for a sea - son, To re-ceive a name
3. Bore it up tri - umph - ant, With its hu-man light,

light through all ranks of crea - tures, to the cen - tral
-gain, with his Fa - ther's glo - ry o'er the earth to
Ev' - ry tongue con - fess him King of glo - ry now.
From the lips of sin - ners, Un - to whom he came,
Through all ranks of crea - tures, To the cen - tral height,

height, To the throne, to the Fa - ther's breast,
reign, For all wreaths of em - pire meet up-on his
'Tis the Fa-ther's plea - sure We should call him Lord,
Faith-ful-ly he bore it Spot-less to the last,
To the throne of God - head, To the Fa-ther's breast;

Filled it with the glo-ry of that per - fect rest.
brow, and our hearts con-fess him King of glo - ry now.
Who from the be-gin - ing Was the migh - ty Word.
Brought it back vic-to - rious, When from death he passed;
Filled it with the glo - ry Of that per - fect rest.

4. In your hearts enthrone him:
 There let him subdue
All that is not holy,
 All that is not true:
Crown him as your captain
 In temptation's hour;
Let his will enfold you
 In its light and power.

5. Brothers, this Lord Jesus
 Shall return again,
With his Father's glory
 O'er the earth to reign;
For all wreaths of empire
 Meet upon his brow,
And our hearts confess him
 King of glory now.

46. At the name of Jesus

Caroline M. Noel

'Camberwell'
John M. Brierley

Martially
1-4
p
Last Verse

become...

ruth

songs of wholeness and maturity

47. I want to walk with Jesus Christ

St. Paul's Erith 1964 Houseparty

Swiss folk tune
Arr. Betty Pulkingham

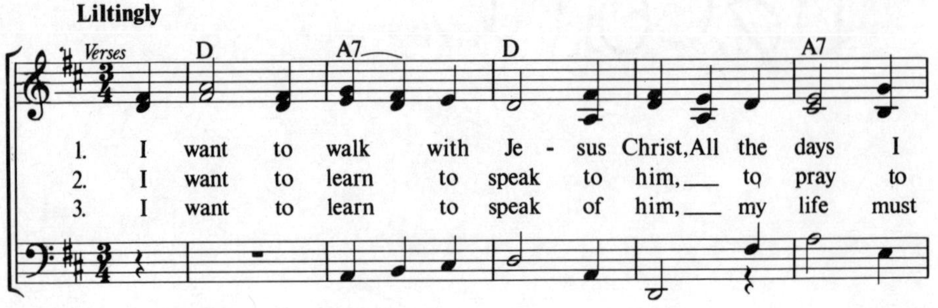
Liltingly
Verses
D A7 D A7
1. I want to walk with Je - sus Christ, All the days I
2. I want to learn to speak to him,__ to pray to
3. I want to learn to speak of him,__ my life must

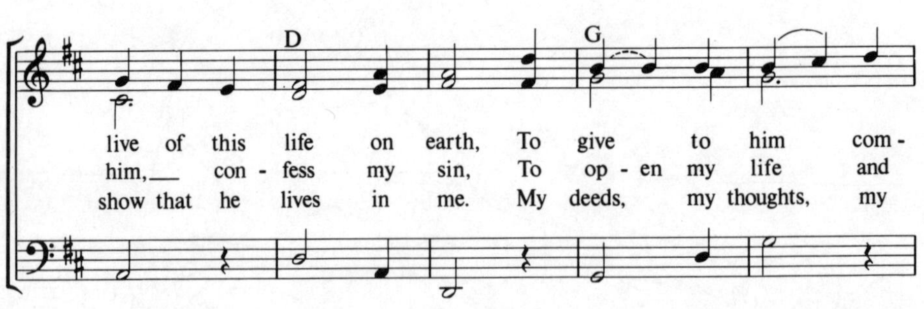
D G
live of this life on earth, To give to him com -
him,__ con - fess my sin, To op - en my life and
show that he lives in me. My deeds, my thoughts, my

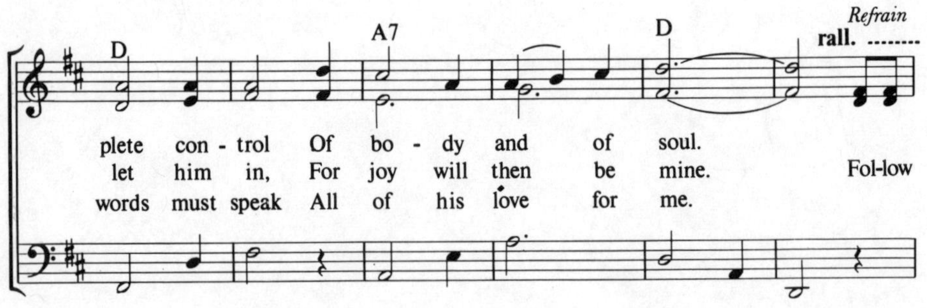
D A7 D
Refrain
rall.
plete con - trol Of bo - dy and of soul.
let him in, For joy will then be mine. Fol-low
words must speak All of his love for me.

A7
D
a tempo, well accented
A7
him, fol-low him, yield your life to him, he has con - quered

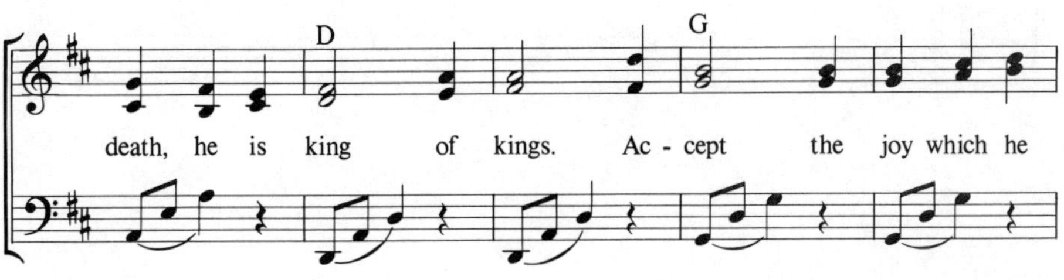
D
G
death, he is king of kings. Ac - cept the joy which he

D
A7
D
gives to those who yield their lives to him.

4. I want to learn to read his word,
   For this is how I know the way
   To live my life as pleases him,
   In holiness and joy.

5. O Holy Spirit of the Lord,
   Enter now into this heart of mine,
   Take full control of my selfish will
   And make me wholly thine.

48. How sweet the name of Jesus sounds

John Newton

Gary Miles

Tenderly, in unison

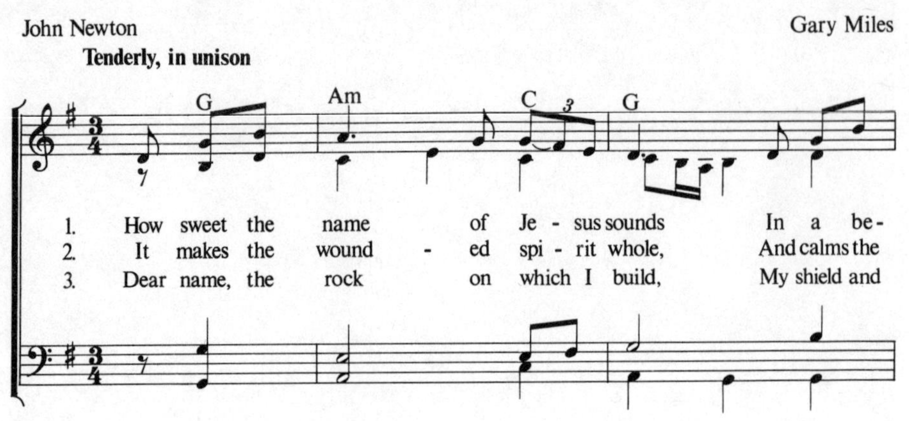
G
Am
C
3
G
1. How sweet the name of Je - sus sounds In a be-
2. It makes the wound - ed spi - rit whole, And calms the
3. Dear name, the rock on which I build, My shield and

Bm7
CM7
D
Em
C
3
liev - er's ear! It soothes his sor - rows, heals his
trou - bled breast; 'Tis man - na to the hun - gry
hid - ing place, My nev - er - fail - ing treas - 'ry,

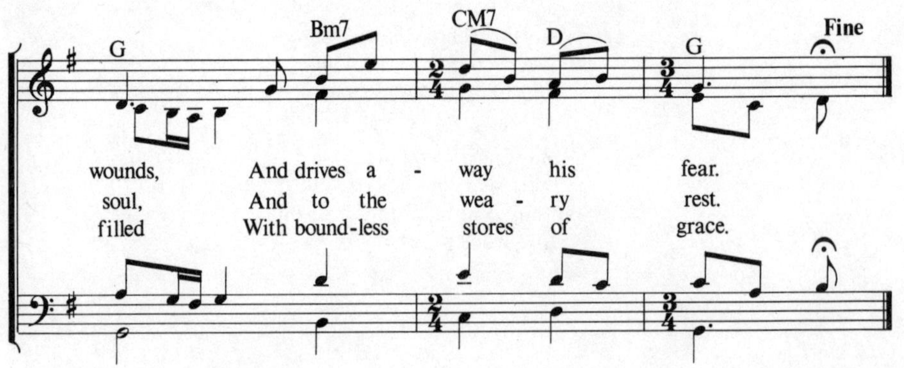
G
Bm7
CM7
D
G
Fine
wounds, And drives a - way his fear.
soul, And to the wea - ry rest.
filled With bound-less stores of grace.

4. Jesus! my Shepherd, Brother, Friend,
   My Prophet, Priest, and King,
My Lord, my Life, my Way, my End,
   Accept the praise I bring.

5. Weak is the effort of my heart,
   And cold my warmest thought;
But when I see thee as thou art,
   I'll praise thee as I ought.

6. Till then I would thy love proclaim
   With every fleeting breath;
And may the music of thy name
   Refresh my soul in death.

Optional interlude

49. Here comes Jesus

Anon.
Arr. Betty Pulkingham

Slowly
C
Here comes Je - sus, see him walk-ing on the
F
wa - ter,
he'll lift you
C
up
and he'll help you to
G7
stand.
Here comes
C
Je - sus,
he's the master of the waves
F
that roll.

C G7 C
Here comes Je - sus, he'll make you whole.
Moving ahead faster
A7 D
Here comes Je - sus, see him walk-ing on the
G D
wa - ter, he'll lift you up and he'll help you to
A7 D
stand. Here comes Je - sus,

G
he's the master of the waves that roll.
Here comes
D
A7
D
Je - sus,
he'll make you whole.
Still faster!
B7
E
Here comes Je - sus,
see him walk-ing on the
A
E
wa - ter,
he'll lift you up
and he'll help you to

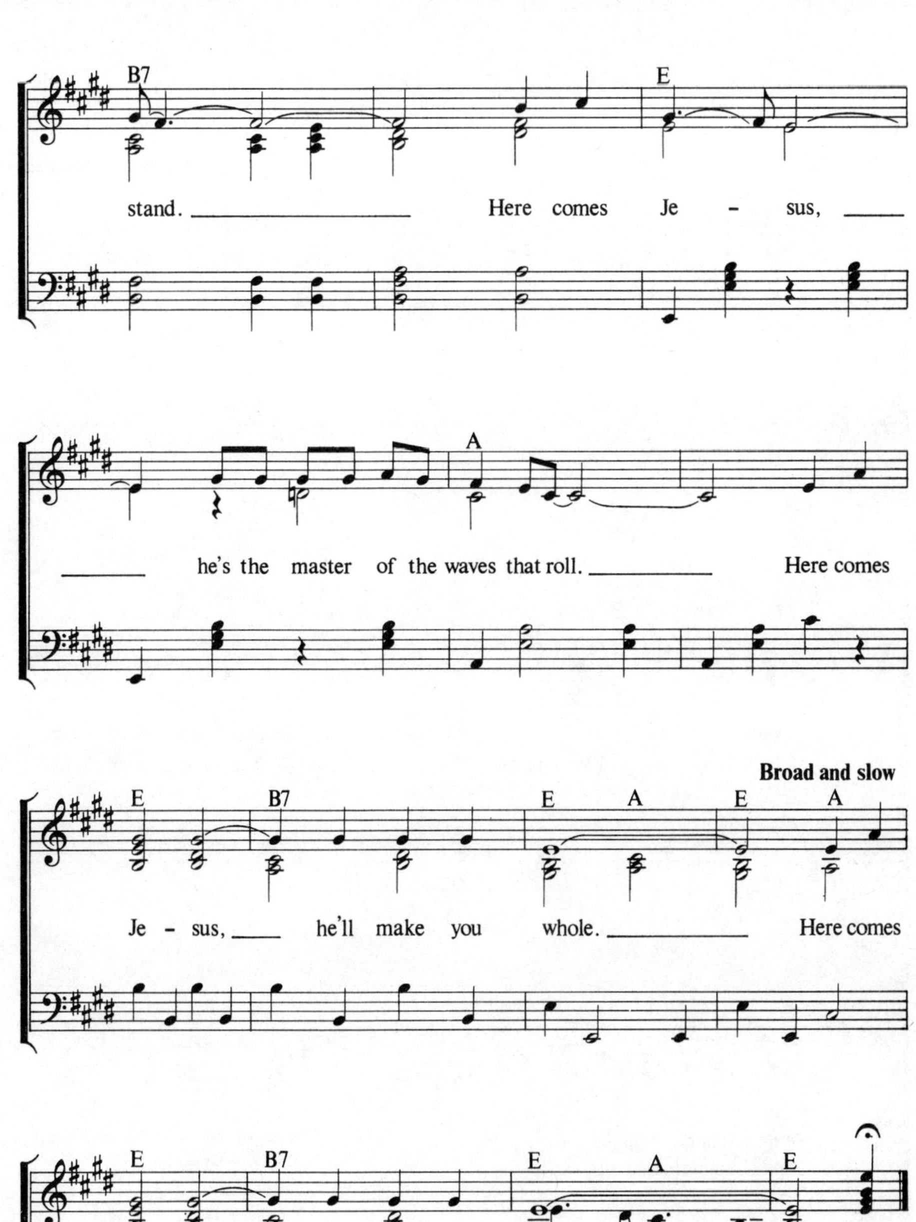
B7
E
stand. Here comes Je - sus,
he's the master of the waves that roll. Here comes
A
Broad and slow
E
B7
E
A
E
A
Je - sus, he'll make you whole. Here comes
E
B7
E
A
E
Je - sus, he'll save your soul.

50. Silver and gold have I none

Anon.

Rollicking *Arr.* Betty Pulkingham

G C Am D7

Verse: Pe - ter and John went to pray, they met a lame man on the
Refrain: 'Sil - ver and gold have I none, but such as I have give I

G G7 C Am

way. He asked for alms and held out his palms, and
thee, in the name of Je - sus Christ ______ of

D7
1. G
2. G
this is what Pe - ter did say:
Naz - a-reth, rise up and walk!' He went

D7
walk - ing and leap - ing and prais - ing God,
G
walk - ing and leap - ing and prais - ing God. 'In the
C
Am
name of Je - sus Christ of
D7
G
Naz - a-reth, rise up and walk.'

51. There is a balm in Gilead

Capo 1 (E)
North American spiritual
Arr. Betty Pulkingham
Easily, not fast
Refrain
F(E)
There is a balm in Gil - e - ad to make the wounded
C7(B7)
F(E)
whole. There is a balm in Gil - e - ad to
B♭M7(AM7)
C7(B7)
F(E)
Fine
Verses
F(E)
heal the sin - sick soul.
1. Some - times I feel dis -
2. If you can - not sing like
Gm(F♯m)
F(E)
C7(B7)
F(E)
couraged, and think my work's in vain, but then the Ho - ly
an - gels, if you can - not preach like Paul, you can tell the love of
Gm(F♯m)
B♭M7(AM7)
C7(B7)
F(E)
B♭(A)
C7(B7)
Spi - rit re - vives my soul a - gain. There is a
Je - sus and say he died for all.

52. Dear Lord and Father

John Greenleaf Whittier

'Repton'
Charles H. Parry

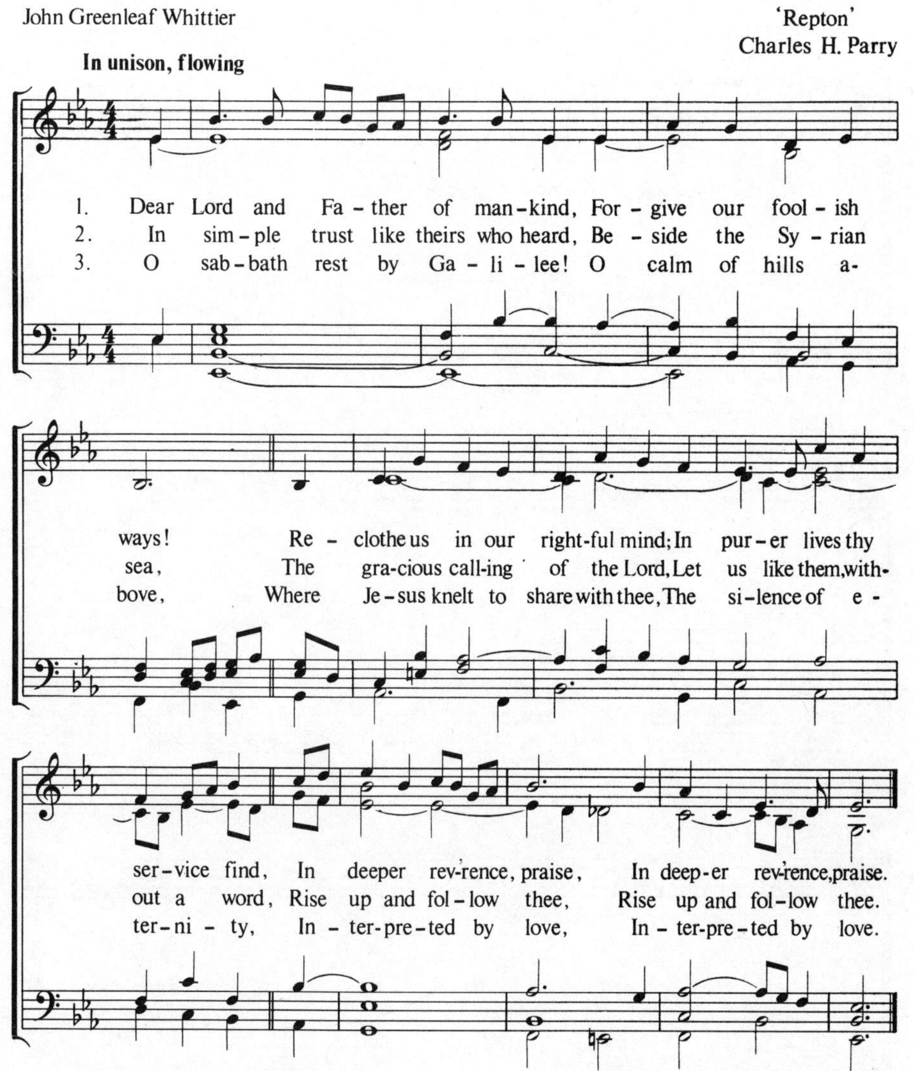
In unison, flowing
1. Dear Lord and Fa - ther of man-kind, For - give our fool - ish ways! Re - clothe us in our right-ful mind; In pur - er lives thy ser - vice find, In deeper rev'rence, praise, In deep-er rev'rence, praise.
2. In sim - ple trust like theirs who heard, Be - side the Sy - rian sea, The gra-cious call-ing of the Lord, Let us like them, with-out a word, Rise up and fol - low thee, Rise up and fol - low thee.
3. O sab - bath rest by Ga - li - lee! O calm of hills a-bove, Where Je - sus knelt to share with thee, The si - lence of e - ter - ni - ty, In - ter - pre - ted by love, In - ter - pre - ted by love.

4. With that deep hush subduing all
 Our words and works that drown
The tender whisper of thy call,
As noiseless let thy blessing fall
 As fell thy manna down.

5. Drop thy still dews of quietness
 Till all our strivings cease:
Take from our souls the strain and stress,
And let our ordered lives confess
 The beauty of thy peace.

6. Breathe through the heats of our desire
 Thy coolness and thy balm;
Let sense be dumb—let flesh retire;
Speak through the earthquake, wind, and fire,
 O still small voice of calm!

53. The bell song*

David Lynch
Arr. Betty Pulkingham

With quiet joy

E

1. You got-ta have love ______ in your heart. ______ You got-ta have love ______ in your heart. ______ You knew it was
peace ______ on your mind. ______ You got-ta have peace ______ on your mind. ______ You knew it was
joy ______ in your soul. ______ You got-ta have joy ______ in your soul. ______ The love__ of
la ______ la la la *etc.*

* The Trees Group conceived this song as a delicate expression of praise through the use of bells and other small percussion instruments. Even a set of keys or a few coins from your pocket can be 'jingled' to add to the happy sound.

Suggested strum for guitar: the following rhythm with open strings sounding at ▼

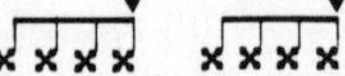

A
E
Je - sus right from the start.
Je - sus there all the time.
Je - sus will make you whole.
D
A
You got-ta have love in your heart.
You got-ta have peace on your mind.
You got-ta have joy in your soul.
E
1.-4.
5.
2. You got-ta have
3. You got-ta have
4. La la la la
You got-ta know
D
A
E
(repeat ad lib.)
Fine
Je - - - sus in your heart.

54. By your stripes

Based on Isaiah 53: 5

Pamela Greenwood
Arr. Jeanne Harper

Boldly
C
F
By your stripes, Lord, I'm healed, hal - le - lu - jah! In your
G7
C
word it is re-vealed, hal - le - lu - jah! Yes, you
F
bore it all for me on the cross of Cal - va - ry so that
G
C
now I can go free, hal - le - lu - jah!

songs of the kingdom (the Body of Christ)

including songs for Holy Communion

55. Alleluia! sing to Jesus

William Dix

'Hyfrydol'
Rowland Prichard
Descant by Betty Pulkingham

With dignity

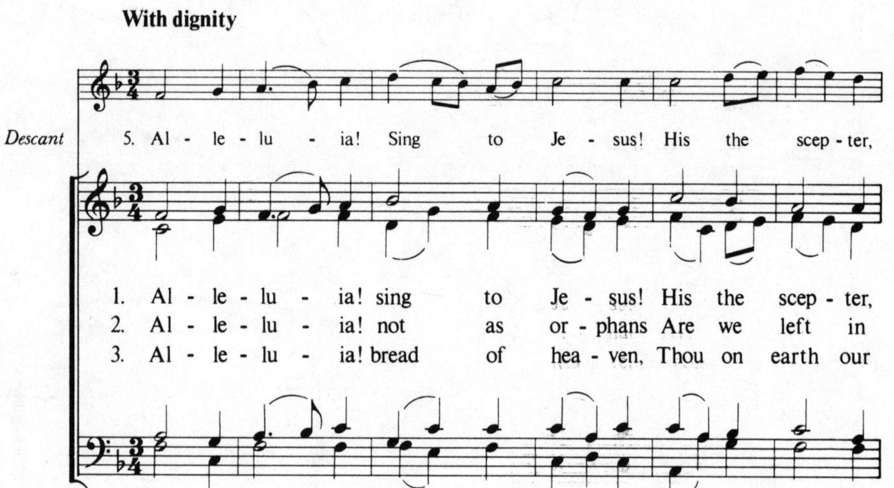
Descant
5. Al - le - lu - ia! Sing to Je - sus! His the scep - ter,
1. Al - le - lu - ia! sing to Je - sus! His the scep - ter,
2. Al - le - lu - ia! not as or - phans Are we left in
3. Al - le - lu - ia! bread of hea - ven, Thou on earth our

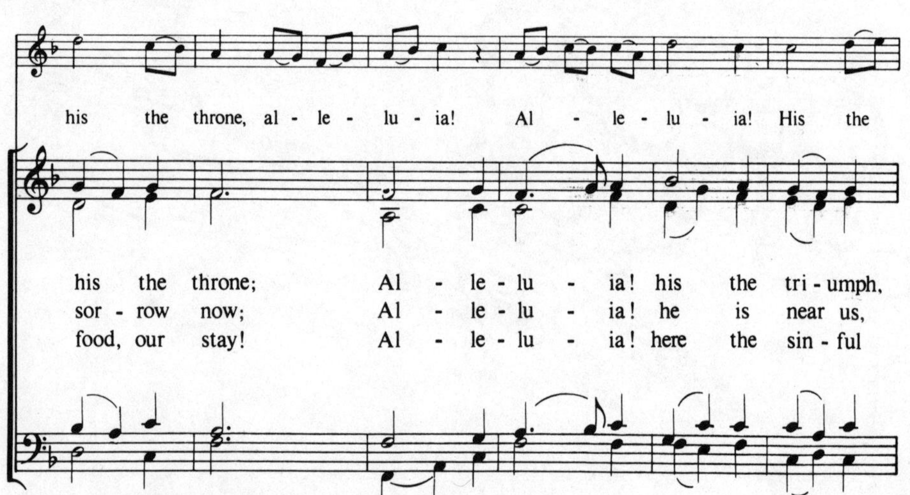
his the throne, al - le - lu - ia! Al - le - lu - ia! His the
his the throne; Al - le - lu - ia! his the tri - umph,
sor - row now; Al - le - lu - ia! he is near us,
food, our stay! Al - le - lu - ia! here the sin - ful

Harmonization based on the English Hymnal version by R. Vaughan Williams (1872-1958) by permission of Oxford University Press.

vic - to - ry, the vic - t'ry a - lone. Al - le - lu - ia! Al - le - lu -
His the vic - to - ry a - lone; Hark! the songs of peace - ful
Faith be - lieves, nor ques-tions how: Though the cloud from sight re -
Flee to thee from day to day: In - ter - ces - sor, friend of
ia! Al - le - lu - ia! Al-le - lu - ia! Al - le -
Zi - on Thun - der like a migh - ty flood; Je - sus
ceived him, When the for - ty days were o'er, Shall our
sin - ners, Earth's re - deem - er, plead for me, Where the
lu - ia! Al - - le - lu - ia! Al - le - lu - - ia!
out of ev - 'ry na - tion Hath re - deemed us by his blood.
hearts for - get his prom - ise, 'I am with you ev - er more?'
songs of all the sin - less Sweep a - cross the crys - tal sea.

4. Alleluia! king eternal,
    Thee the Lord of lords we own:
Alleluia! born of Mary,
    Earth thy footstool, heav'n thy throne:
Thou within the veil hast entered,
    Robed in flesh, our great high priest:
Thou on earth both priest and victim
    In the eucharistic feast.

5. Alleluia! sing to Jesus!
    His the scepter, his the throne;
Alleluia! his the triumph,
    His the victory alone;
Hark! the songs of holy Zion
    Thunder like a mighty flood;
Jesus out of every nation
    Hath redeemed us by his blood.

56. Blow, thou cleansing wind

Alan Teage

'Hyfrydol'
Rowland Prichard

1. Blow, thou cleansing wind from heaven,
    Burn, thou fire, within our hearts.
Spirit of the Lord, possess us,
    Fill our lives in every part.
Mind of Christ, be thou our ruler,
    Word of truth, be thou our guide;
Leave no part of us unhallowed.
    Come, O come in us abide.

2. Fill thy church, inspire and strengthen,
    Chasten, mould, empower and lead.
Make us one, and make us joyful,
    Give us grace for every need.
Be our life, build firm thy kingdom.
    Be our strength, who are but frail.
Then indeed against us never
    Shall the gates of hell prevail.

3. Win the world! Baptize the nations!
    Open every blinded eye.
Leave no sinner unconvicted;
    Leave no soul untouched and dry.
Conquering love, take thou the kingdom,
    Rule thou over all our days;
Then in glory and rejoicing
    Earth shall echo with thy praise.

57. Jesus

Debby Kerner
Arr. Betty Pulkingham

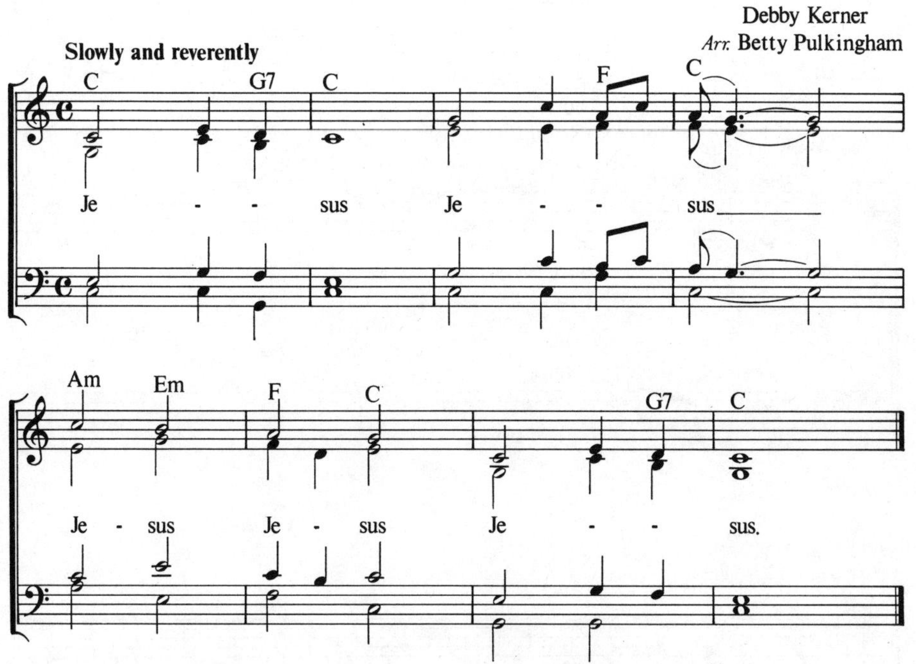
Slowly and reverently
C G7 C F C
Je - - sus Je - - sus
Am Em F C G7 C
Je - sus Je - sus Je - - sus.

2. He died. 3. He rose. 4. He lives. 5. We live through him. *Repeat v.l.*

58. Seek ye first

(2-part round)

Karen Lafferty

Rich and broad
1 D F♯m G D G D A sus 4-3
Seek ye first the King-dom of God, and his righteous - ness,
D F♯m G D G D
and all these things shall be add-ed un-to you; al - le - lu, al - le-
A7 D 2 D F♯m G D G D Asus 4 - 3
lu - ia. Al - le - lu - ia, al - le - lu - ia,
D F♯m G D G D A7 D
al - le - lu - ia, al - le - lu, al-le - lu - ia.

59. Fear not! rejoice and be glad

Adapted from Joel 2,3,4. Priscilla Wright

With breadth

Refrain
Em
Fear not, re - joice and be glad, the

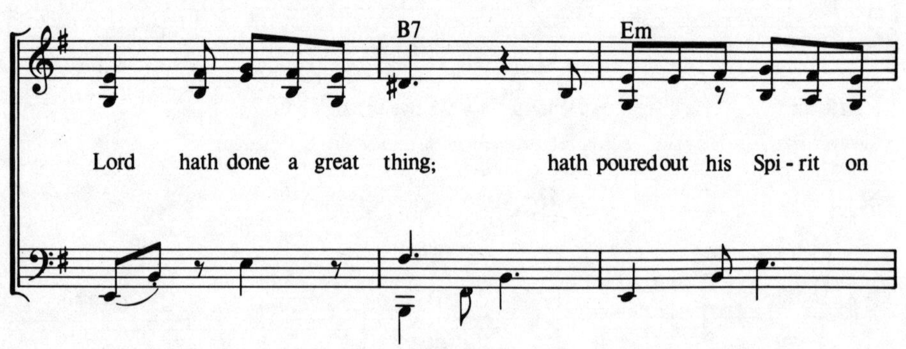
B7
Em
Lord hath done a great thing; hath poured out his Spi - rit on

Am
Em
B7
Em
Fine
Verses
all man - kind, on those who con - fess his name.
1. The
2. Ye
3. My
4. My

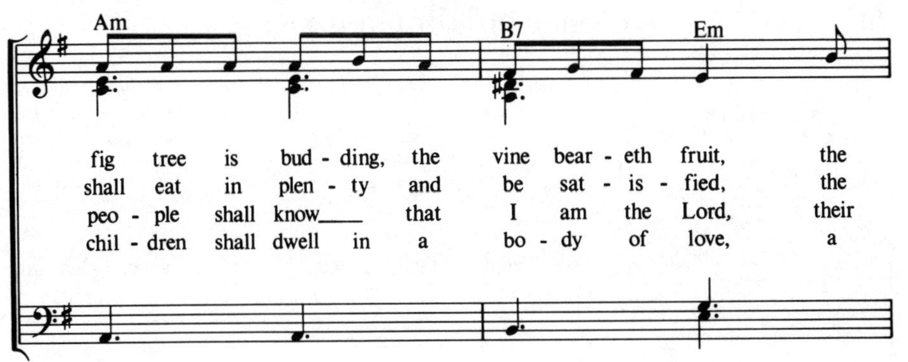
Am
B7
Em
fig tree is bud - ding, the vine bear - eth fruit, the
shall eat in plen - ty and be sat - is - fied, the
peo - ple shall know___ that I am the Lord, their
chil - dren shall dwell in a bo - dy of love, a

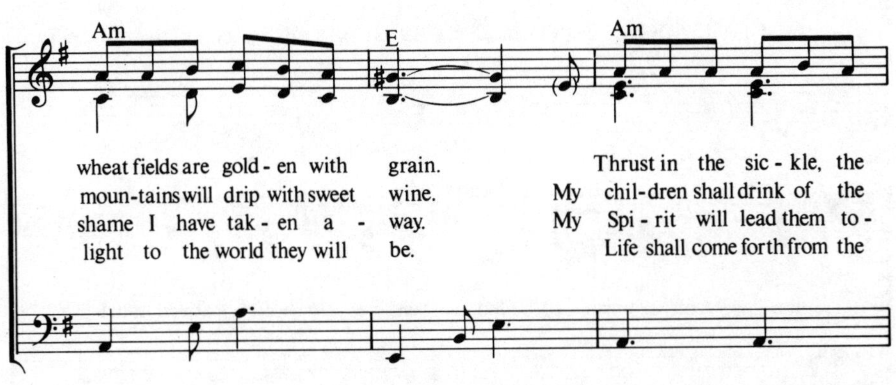
Am
E
Am
wheat fields are gold - en with grain. Thrust in the sic - kle, the
moun-tains will drip with sweet wine. My chil-dren shall drink of the
shame I have tak - en a - way. My Spi - rit will lead them to -
light to the world they will be. Life shall come forth from the

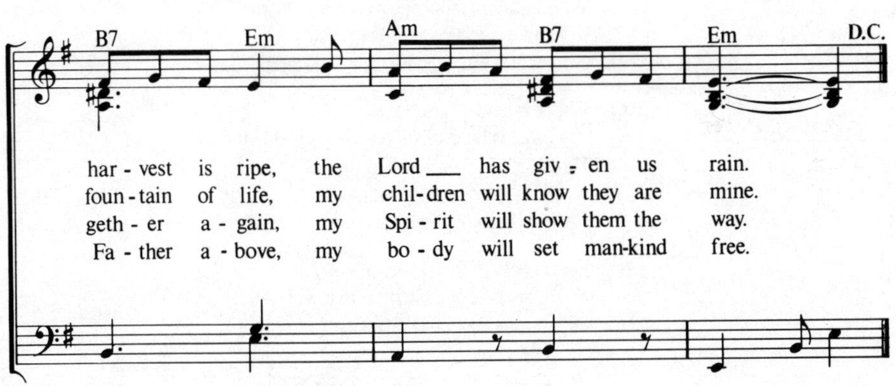
B7
Em
Am
B7
Em
D.C.
har - vest is ripe, the Lord___ has giv - en us rain.
foun - tain of life, my chil-dren will know they are mine.
geth - er a - gain, my Spi - rit will show them the way.
Fa - ther a - bove, my bo - dy will set man-kind free.

60. God is building a house

Verses 2,3,4 – Hong Sit

Anon.
Arr. Betty Pulkingham

Well-accented
E
E7
A
1. God is build-ing a house, God is build-ing a house, God is
E
B7
E
E7
build-ing a house that will stand. He is build-ing by his plan with the
A
E
B7
E
live - ly stones of man, God is build-ing a house that will stand.

2. God is building a house, *(repeat)*
   God is building a house that will stand.
   With apostles, prophets, pastors,
   With evangelists and teachers,
   God is building a house that will stand.

3. Christ is head of this house, *(repeat)*
   Christ is head of this house that will stand.
   He abideth in its praise,
   Will perfect it in its ways,
   Christ is head of this house that will stand.

4. We are part of this house, *(repeat)*
   We are part of this house that will stand.
   We are called from ev'ry nation
   To enjoy his full salvation,
   We are part of this house that will stand.

61.
The kingdom of God

Brian Howard
Bright and cheerful, not too fast
A
D
A
1. The king - dom of God is neith - er lo here, nor
4. The Spir - it of God was not lost af - ter
5. The Prince of Peace has not gone a - way, He won't
6. The joy of the Lord is like a sing - ing lark, deep with-
D
A
E
lo there, no, the king - dom is a-
Pente - cost, no, the Spir - it is a-
let you stray, no, the Prince of Peace is a-
in your heart, let it flow so free - ly a-
1
A
2
A
mong us. The mong us.

2. The vict'ry of God is neither lo here, nor lo there,
No, the vict'ry is among us.

3. The power of God is neither lo here, nor lo there,
No, the power is among us.

63. I am the bread of life

S. Suzanne Toolan
Arr. Betty Pulkingham

Capo 3 (G)
Rich and full

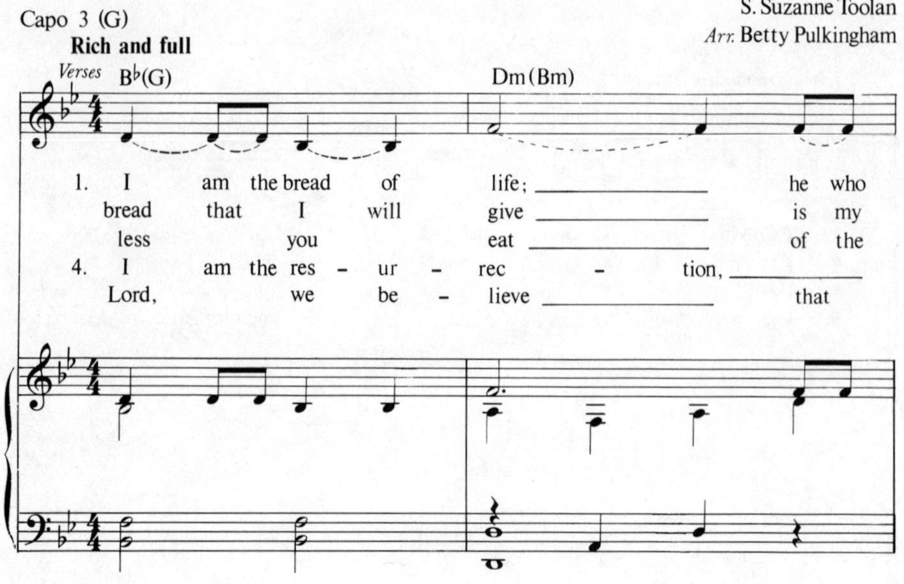
Verses
B♭(G)
Dm(Bm)
1. I am the bread of life; he who
bread that I will give is my
less you eat of the
4. I am the res - ur - rec - tion,
Lord, we be - lieve that

E♭(C)
F(D)
comes to me shall not hun - ger; he who be-
flesh for the life of the world and he who
flesh of the Son of man and
I am the life. He who be-
you are the Christ, the

B♭(G) Dm(Bm) E♭(C) B♭(G)
lieves in me shall not thirst. No one can come to
eats of this bread, he shall live for-
drink of his blood, and drink of his
lieves in me, ev - en if he,
Son of God who has
E♭(C) Cm(Am) F(D)
Refrain
me un - less the Fa - ther draw him.
ev - er, he shall live for ev - er.
blood you shall not have life with - in you.
die, he shall live for - ev - er.
come in - to the world.
And I will
B♭(G) F(D) B♭(G) E♭(C)
raise him up, and I will raise him

F(D)
B♭(G)
E♭(C)
up, and I will raise him up on the
B♭(G)
F(D)
1-4
B♭(G)
final ending
B♭(G)
last day.
2. The
3. Un -
5. Yes,
day.

64. Oh, the blood of Jesus

Anon.
Arr. Betty Pulkingham

Capo 1 (E)

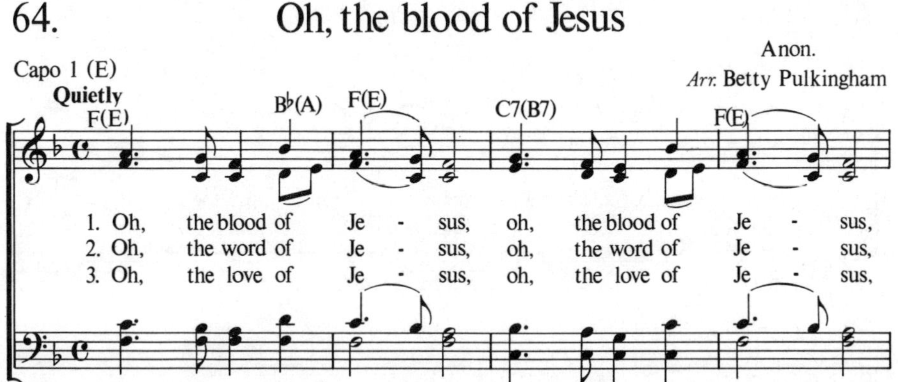
Quietly
F(E)
B♭(A)
F(E)
C7(B7)
F(E)
1. Oh, the blood of Je - sus, oh, the blood of Je - sus,
2. Oh, the word of Je - sus, oh, the word of Je - sus,
3. Oh, the love of Je - sus, oh, the love of Je - sus,

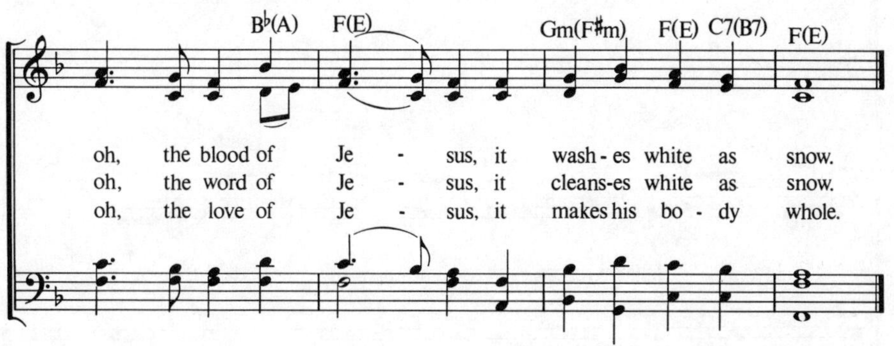
B♭(A)
F(E)
Gm(F♯m)
F(E)
C7(B7)
F(E)
oh, the blood of Je - sus, it wash - es white as snow.
oh, the word of Je - sus, it cleans-es white as snow.
oh, the love of Je - sus, it makes his bo - dy whole.

'Oh, the blood of Jesus' may be sung in sequence with the following:

65. At the cross

Capo 1 (E)

Sankey
Arr. Betty Pulkingham

Smoothly
F(E)
C7(B7)
At the cross, at the cross where I first saw the light, And the
F(E)
F7(E7)
B♭(A)
bur-den of my heart rolled a - way, It was there by faith I re-
F(E)
C7(B7)
F(E) B♭(A) F(E)
ceived my sight, And now I am hap - py all the day.

66. A new commandment

John 13: 34 - 35

Anon.
Arr. Betty Pulkingham

Warmly
D Bm Em7
A new com - mand-ment I give un - to
A7 D Bm Em7
you, that you love one an - oth - er as I have loved
A7 F#m Bm Em A7
you, that you love one an - oth - er as I have loved
D D7 G A7 D A
you. By this shall all men know you are my dis-

Bm
G
A
Bm
3
G
D
ci - ples if you have love one to an - oth - er.

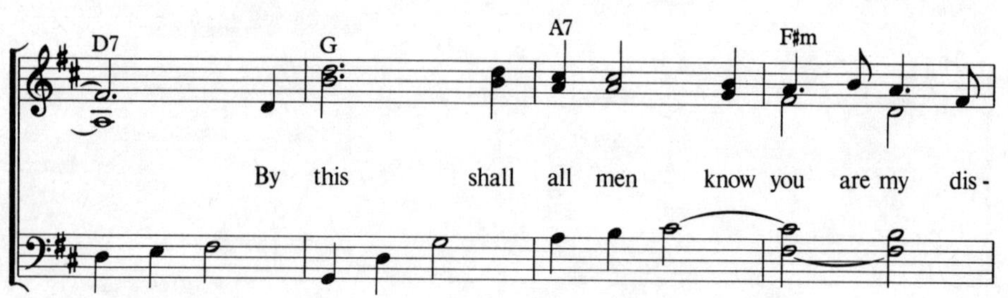
D7
G
A7
F♯m
By this shall all men know you are my dis -

Bm
Em
A
Bm
3
G
D
ci - ples if you have love one to an - oth - er.
3

67. God and man at table are sat down

Robert Stamps
Arr. Jeanne Harper

With dignity and gentleness
Em Bm7 Em
1. Oh wel-come, all ye no-ble saints of old As
2. El-ders, mar-tyrs, all are fall-ing down,
3. Who is this who spreads the vic-t'ry feast?
D A7 D B7
now be-fore your ve-ry eyes un-fold The
Pro-phets, pa-tri-archs are gath-'ring round. What
Who is this who makes our war-ring cease?
Em B7 Em
won-ders all so long a-go fore-told:
an-gels longed to see now man has found.
Je-sus, ri-sen Sa-viour, Prince of Peace.
Am7 Bm7 1. Em 2. Em
God and man at ta-ble are sat down. down.

4. Beggars, lame and harlots
also here;
Re/pentant publicans are
drawing near,
Wayward sons come home
without a fear.
God and man at table are
sat down. *(repeat)*

5. Worship in the presence of
the Lord
With / joyful songs and hearts
in one accord
And / let our host at table be
adored.
God and man at table are
sat down. *(repeat)*

6. When at last this earth shall pass away,
When / Jesus and his bride are one to stay,
The / feast of love is just begun that day.
God and man at table are sat down. *(repeat)*

68. Glory be to Jesus

'Caswall'

Tr. Edward Caswall

Friedrick Filitz

Descant Betty Pulkingham

With breadth
1. Glo - ry be to Je - sus, Who in bit - ter pains
2. Grace and life e - ter - nal In that blood I find,
3. Blest through end - less a - ges Be the pre - cious stream
Poured for me the life blood From his sa - cred veins!
Blest be his com - pas - sion In - fi - nite - ly kind!
Which from sin and sor - row Doth the world re - deem!

4. Oft as earth exulting
Wafts its praise on high,
Angel hosts, rejoicing,
Make their glad reply.

*5. Lift ye then your voices;
Swell the mighty flood;
Louder still and louder
Praise the precious blood.

*Optional descant on page 117

Optional descant last stanza
5. Lift ye then your voi - ces; Swell the migh - ty flood;
Loud - er still and loud - er Praise the pre - cious blood.

69. We really want to thank you, Lord

Capo 2(C)

Ed Baggett
Arr. Betty Pulkingham

With a swing

Refrain

D(C) F♯m(Em) G(F) A(G)

We real - ly want to thank you, Lord.
We real - ly want to bless your name.

D(C) F♯m(Em) G(F) A(G) *last time* ⊕ D(C) F♯m(Em)

Hal - le - lu - jah! Je - sus is our king! ______

1.G(F) A(G) 2.G(F) A(G) *Verse* D(C) F♯m(Em)

1. We thank you, Lord, for your
2. We thank you, Lord, for our

G(F)
A(G)
D(C)
F#m (Em)
G(F)
A(G)
gift to us, your life so rich be - yond com - pare, the
life to-geth - er, to live and move in the love of Christ,
D(C)
F#m (Em)
G(F)
A(G)
gift of your bo - dy here on earth of
ten - der - ness which sets us free to
D(C)
G(F)
A(G)
Refrain
which we sing and share.
serve you with our lives.
D(C)
G(F)
D(C)
king!

This is my commandment

John 15: 11-12

Anon
Arr. Betty Pulkingham

Simply

E

This is my command-ment that you love one an-oth - er, that your

B7 | 1 E *Fine* | 2 E

joy may be full. full; that your

A E

joy ___ may be full, ___ that your

A E *D.C. al Fine*

joy ___ may be full, ___

Other verses may be added:
eg. This is my commandment that you 'trust one another…'
'serve one another…'
'lay down your lives…'

71. The king of love

H.W. Baker
Based on Psalm 23

'St. Columba'
Traditional Irish melody

In flowing style

❄ D D A D A7 Bm7 F♯m G 3 A (Em)
1. The king of love my shep-herd is, Whose good-ness fail - eth nev -
2. Where streams of liv - ing wa - ter flow, My ransomed soul he lead -
3. Per - verse and fool - ish oft I strayed, But yet in love he sought

A7 Bm7 G A Bm7 Em A A7 D (G) D
- er; I noth - ing lack if I am his, And he is mine for ev - er.
- eth, And where the ver - dant pas - tures grow, With food ce - les - tial feed - eth.
me, And on his shoul - der gen - tly laid, And home, re - joic - ing, brought me.

4. In death's dark vale I fear no ill
   With thee, dear Lord, beside me;
Thy rod and staff my comfort still,
   Thy cross before to guide me.

5. Thou spread'st a table in my sight;
   Thy unction grace bestoweth;
And o what transport of delight
   From thy pure chalice floweth!

6. And so through all the length of days
   Thy goodness faileth never:
Good shepherd, may I sing thy praise
   Within thy house for ever.

❄Guitar chords and 4-part harmonization not designed to be used together.

72. Glorious things of thee are spoken

John Newton

'Abbot's Leigh'
Cyril Taylor

Majestic
1. Glor - ious things of thee are spo - ken, Zi - on
2. See the streams of liv - ing wat - ers, Spring - ing
3. Round each hab - it - a - tion hov' ring, See the

ci - ty of our God. He whose word can -
from e - ter - nal love, Well sup - ply thy
cloud and fire ap - pear! For a glo - ry

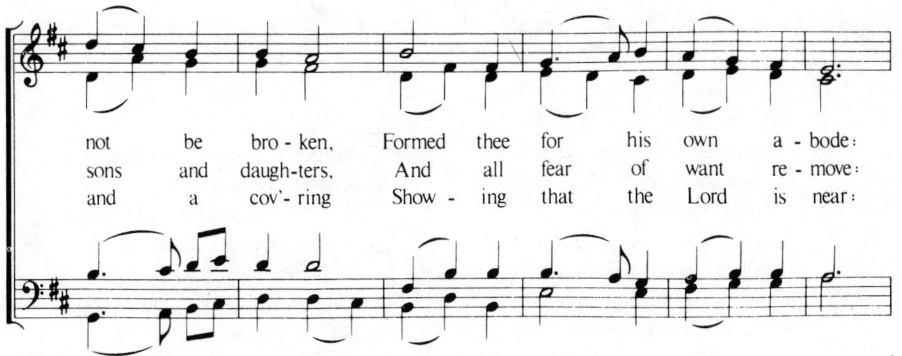
not be bro - ken, Formed thee for his own a - bode:
sons and daugh-ters, And all fear of want re - move:
and a cov'- ring Show - ing that the Lord is near:

From the *BBC Hymn Book* by permission of Oxford University Press.

On the rock of ag - es found - ed, What can
Who can faint while such a riv - er Ev - er
He who gives them dai - ly man - na, He who
shake thy sure re - pose? With sal - va - tion's
flows their thirst to assuage? Grace which like the
list - ens when they cry: Let him hear the
walls sur - round - ed, Thou may'st smile at all thy foes.
Lord, the giv - er, Ev - er flows from age to age.
loud hos - an - na, Ri - sing to his throne on high.

4. Saviour since of Zion's city
   I through grace a member am,
Let the world deride or pity,
   I will glory in thy name;
Fading is the worldling's pleasure,
   All his boasted pomp and show;
Solid joys and lasting treasure
   None but Zion's children know.

5. Blest inhabitants of Zion;
   Washed in the Redeemer's blood!
Jesus, whom their souls rely on,
   Makes them kings and priests to God.
'Tis his love his people raises
   Over self to reign as kings:
And as priests, his solemn praises
   Each for a thank-off'ring brings.

72. Glorious things of thee are spoken

'Austria'
Franz Joseph Haydn

Majestic

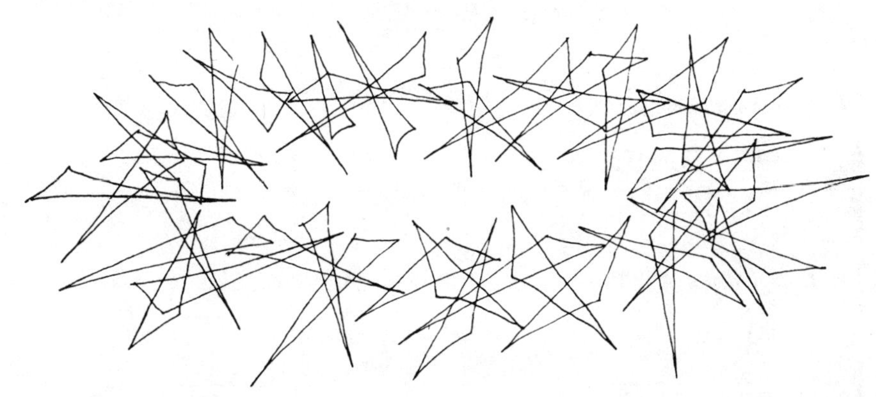

suffer-reign

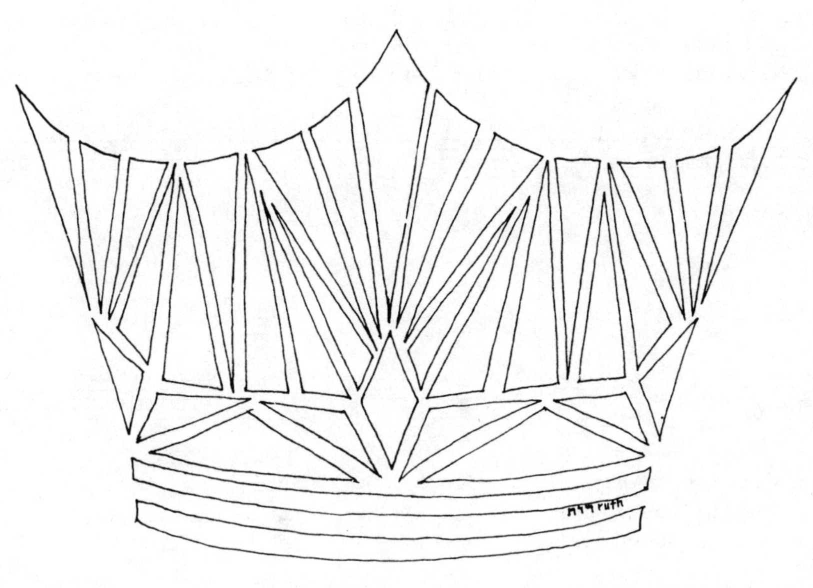

songs of faith and victory

74. God has called you

Diane Davis

Soft and unhurried

C
F
C
1. God has called (name), he will not fail (him, her).
2. God has called you, he will not fail you.
3. God has called us, we will not fail him.

G
G7
C
God has called(name), he will not fail (him, her).
God has called you, he will not fail you.
God has called us, we will not fail him.

F
C
God has called (name), he will not fail (him, her), so
God has called you, he will not fail you, so
God has called us, we will not fail him, so

G
G7
C
1-2
1-3: trust in God and o - bey him.

final ending
G
G7
C
So trust in God and o - bey him.

75. How firm a foundation

John Rippon

'Lyons'
Based on Michael Haydn

With energy
1. How firm a foun - da - tion, ye saints of the Lord, is laid for your faith in his ex - cel - lent word! What more can he say than to you he hath said, To you that for ref - uge to Je - sus have fled?
2. 'Fear not, I am with thee; O be not dis-mayed! For I am thy God, and will still give thee aid; I'll strength - en thee, help thee, and cause thee to stand, Up - held by my right-eous, om - ni - po - tent hand.
3. 'When through the deep wa - ters I call thee to go, The riv - ers of woe shall not thee o - ver - flow; For I will be with thee, thy trou - bles to bless, And sanc - ti - fy to thee thy deep - est dis - tress.

4. 'When through fiery trials thy pathway shall lie,
My grace, all-sufficient, shall be thy supply;
The flame shall not hurt thee; I only design
Thy dross to consume, and thy gold to refine.

5. 'The soul that to Jesus has fled for repose,
I will not, I will not desert to his foes;
That soul, though all hell shall endeavor to shake,
I'll never, no, never, no, never forsake.'

75. How firm a foundation

Anne Steele

Arr. Betty Pulkingham

With sweeping breadth

D7
G
C
G
C
G
C

D
D7
C
Am7
Bm7
Em
CM7
D

G
Bm7
Em
G

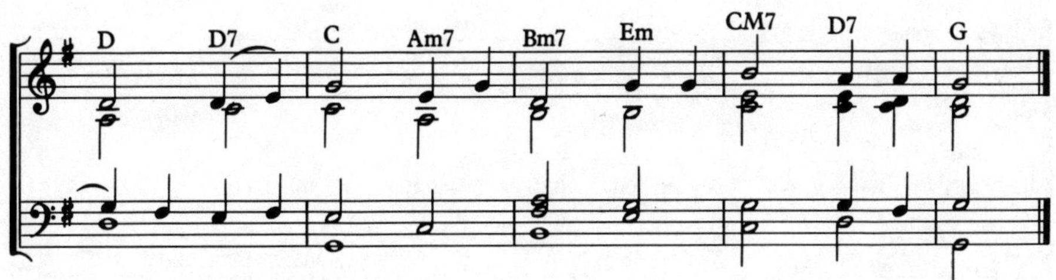
D
D7
C
Am7
Bm7
Em
CM7
D7
G

76. Complete in him

Anon.
Arr. Betty Pulkingham
Well accented
Verses
D
1. The full - ness of the God - head bod-i - ly dwell - eth in my
2. It's not by works of righteous - ness, but by his grace a -
3. There's no - thing more that I can do, for Je - sus did it
A
Lord. The full - ness of the God - head bod-i - ly
lone It's not by works of righteous - ness, but
all. There's no - thing more that I can do, for
D
dwell - eth in my Lord. The full - ness of the God - head bod-i - ly
by his grace a - lone. It's not by works of righteous - ness, but
Je - sus did it all. There's no - thing more that I can do, for
D7 G D A7 D
dwell - eth in my Lord, and
by his grace a - lone, that
Je - sus did it all, and
we are com - plete in him.

Refrain
D
G
D
Com - plete, com-plete, com-plete in him, we are com-
A
D
(Hal - le lu jah, we're)
plete in him. Com-plete, com - plete, com-
G
D
A7
D
plete in him, we are com - plete in him.

77. The Holy Ghost Medley

Capo 3 (A)

Arr. Betty Pulkingham

Well-accented rhythm
C(A)
G(E)
C(A)
Je - sus gave her wa - ter that was not from the well,
C(A)
Am(F♯m)
D7(B7)
G(E)
Gave her liv - ing wa - ter and sent her forth to tell; She
C(A)
F(D)
C(A)
C(A)
F(D)
C(A)
went a-way sing - ing, and came back bring - ing
F(D)
C(A)
G(E)
Fine
C(A)
C7(A7)
oth - ers for the wa - ter that was not from the well.

F(D)
C7(A7)
F(D)
Drink - ing at the springs of liv - ing wa - ter,
C7(A7)
F(D)
Hap - py now am I, My soul is sat - is - fied,
C7(A7)
F(D)
Drink - ing at the springs of liv - ing wa - ter, What a
C7(A7)
F(D)
won - der - ful and boun - te - ous sup - ply. Spring up, O

F(D)
Bb(G)
F(D)
well, with - in my soul. Spring up, O
C(A)
well, and o - ver - flow; Spring up, O
F(D)
Bb(G)
F(D)
well, flow out through me. Spring up, O
C(A)
F(D)
well, set oth - ers free.

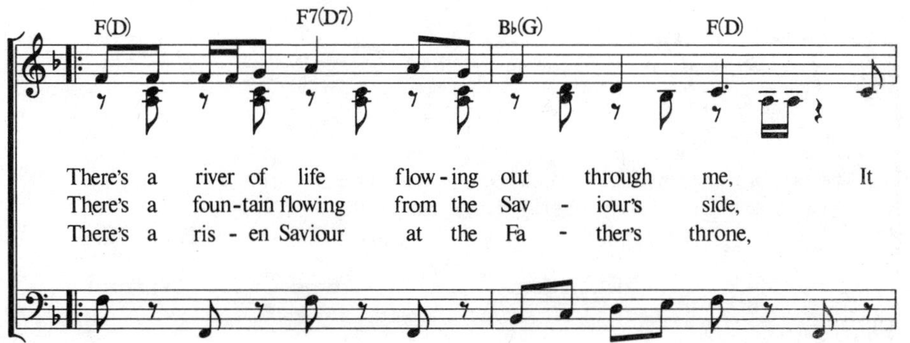
F(D)
F7(D7)
B♭(G)
F(D)
There's a river of life flow-ing out through me, It
There's a foun-tain flowing from the Sav - iour's side,
There's a ris - en Saviour at the Fa - ther's throne,

G7(E7)
C7(A7)
makes the lame to walk and the blind to see,
All my sins for - given in that pre - cious tide.
Ev - er in - ter - ceding for his ve - ry own,

F(D)
B♭(G)
F(D)
O - pens pri - son doors, sets the cap - tives free.
Je - sus paid the price when for me he died.
Pour - ing down the blessings that are his a - lone.

F(D)
C7(A7)
There's a riv - er of life flow - ing out through
There's a foun - tain flow - ing from the Sa - viour's
There's a ris - en Sa - viour at the Fa - ther's
1-5
F(D)
me.
side.
throne.
6
F(D)
me.

4 There's a holy comforter who's sent from heaven,
All the glorious gifts are his, and have been given,
He'll/show us more of Jesus 'til the veil is riven.
There's a holy comforter who's sent from heaven.

5 There's a land of rest that we may enter now,
Freed from all our works and freed from Satan's power,
Just/resting in the Lord each moment and each hour.
There's a land of rest that we may enter now.

6 There's a full salvation wrought for you and me,
From/faith to faith and glory to glory e/ternally,
O/Lord, just take this life and let me live for thee.
There's a full salvation wrought for you and me.

Jesus gave her water – Anon.
Springs of living water – J.W. Peterson

Spring up, o well – Anon.
There's a river of life – L. Casebolt
Verses 2-6 – Betty Carr Pulkingham.

78. I have decided to follow Jesus

Anon
Arr. Betty Pulkingham

With determination
C
1. I have de - cid - ed to fol - low Je - sus. I have de -
2. The world be - hind me, the cross be - fore me. The world be -
3. Tho' none go with me, still I will fol - low. Tho' none go
F
C
cid - ed to fol - low Je - sus. I have de - cid - ed to fol - low
hind me, the cross be - fore me. The world be - hind me, the cross be-
with me, still I will fol - low. Tho' none go with me, still I will
Am
C
G7
C
Je - sus,
fore me,
fol - low,
no turn - ing back, no turn - ing back.

4. Where Jesus leads me, I'll surely follow. *(repeat twice)*
No turning back, no turning back.

5. Sing glory, glory and hallelujah. *(repeat twice)*
No turning back, no turning back.

79. See the conqu'ror mounts in triumph

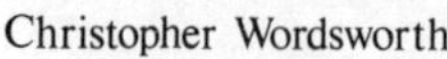

Christopher Wordsworth

'In Babilone'
Traditional Dutch melody

With breadth

1. See the con-qu'ror mounts in tri-umph; See the king in
2. He who on the cross did suf-fer, He who from the
*3. Thou hast raised our hu-man na-ture On the clouds to

roy-al state, Rid-ing on the clouds, his char-iot, To his
grave a-rose, He has vanquished sin and Sa-tan; He by
God's right hand: There we sit in heav'n-ly pla-ces, There with

heav'n-ly pal-ace gate! Hark! the choirs of an-gel
death has spoiled his foes. While he lifts his hands in
thee in glo-ry stand. Je-sus reigns, a-dored by

* Descant page 140

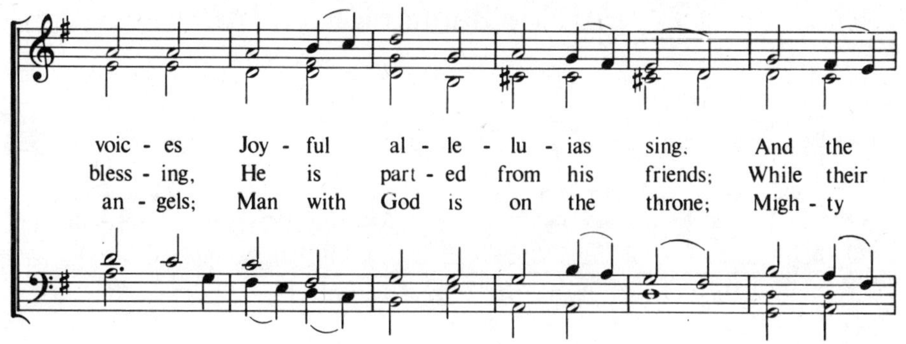
voic - es Joy - ful al - le - lu - ias sing. And the
bless - ing, He is part - ed from his friends; While their
an - gels; Man with God is on the throne; Migh - ty

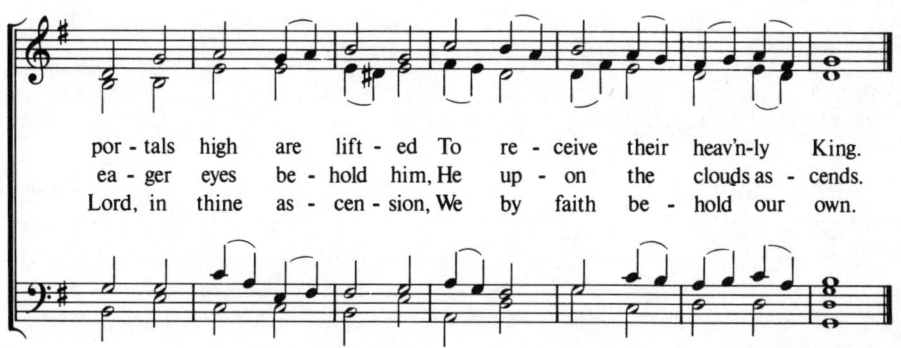
por - tals high are lift - ed To re - ceive their heav'n-ly King.
ea - ger eyes be - hold him, He up - on the clouds as - cends.
Lord, in thine as - cen - sion, We by faith be - hold our own.

80. Hail, thou once despised Jesus

John Blackwell
Martin Madan

'In Babilone'
Traditional Dutch melody

1. Hail, thou once despised Jesus!
Hail, thou Galilean King!
Thou didst suffer to release us;
Thou didst free salvation bring.
Hail, thou universal Saviour,
Bearer of our sin and shame.
By thy merit we find favour:
Life is given through thy name.

2. Paschal Lamb, by God appointed,
All our sins on thee were laid:
By almighty love anointed,
Thou hast full atonement made.
All thy people are forgiven
Through the virtue of thy blood:
Opened is the gate of heaven,
Peace is made 'twixt man and God.

3. Jesus, hail! enthroned in glory,
There for ever to abide;
All the heav'nly hosts adore thee,
Seated at thy Father's side.
There for sinners thou art pleading:
There thou dost our place prepare;
Ever for us interceding,
Till in glory we appear.

*4. Worship, honour, power, and blessing
Thou art worthy to receive:
Highest praises, without ceasing,
Meet it is for us to give.
Help, ye bright angelic spirits,
Bring your sweetest, noblest lays;
Help to sing our Saviour's merits,
Help to chant Emmanuel's praise!

'In Babilone'
(Descant)

Betty Pulkingham

With breadth
Descant
No.79
No.80
Melody
3. Thou hast raised our hu - man na - ture On the clouds to God's right hand. There we sit in heav'n - ly pla - ces, There with thee in glo - ry stand. Jesus reigns adored by an - gels, Man with God is on the throne. Migh-ty Lord, in thine as - cen - sion, We by faith be - hold our own.
4. Wor - ship, hon-our, pow'r and bless-ing Thou art wor - thy to re - ceive. High - est prais - es with - out ceas - ing, Meet it is for us to give. Help ye bright an-gel - ic spi - rits, Bring your sweet - est no-blest lays. Help to sing our Sa - viour's mer - its, Help to chant Em - man - uel's praise.

81. He signed my deed

Anon.
Arr: Betty Pulkingham

Vigorous, well accented
He signed my deed with his a-ton-ing blood, He ev - er lives to
make his prom - ise good. Though all the hosts of hell march in to
make a sec-ond claim, They'll all march out at the men-tion of his name. They'll
[last time, like an echo]
all march out at the men-tion of His name.
Je - sus
(spoken last time)

82. Jesus is Lord

David J. Mansell

With majesty

1. Je - sus is Lord! Cre - a - tion's voice pro - claims it,
2. Je - sus is Lord! Yet from his throne e - ter - nal
3. Je - sus is Lord! O'er sin the migh - ty con - queror,

For by his power each tree and flower was planned and made.
In flesh he came to die in pain on Calv' - ry's tree.
From death he rose and all his foes shall own his name.

Je - sus is Lord! The u - ni - verse de - clares it.
Je - sus is Lord! From him all life pro - ceed - ing,
Je - sus is Lord! God sends his Ho - ly Spir - it

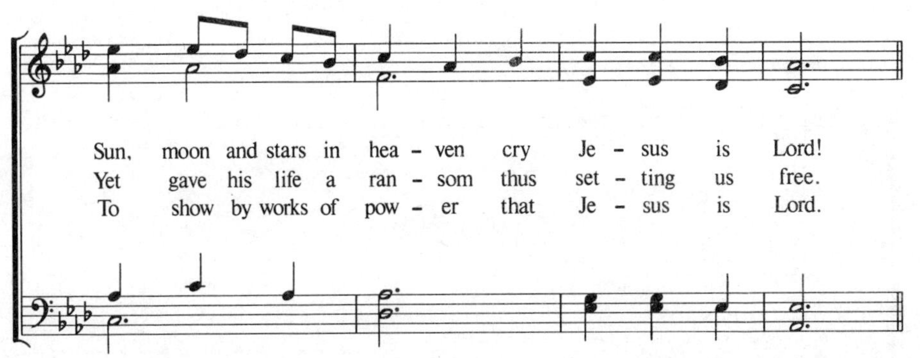
Sun, moon and stars in hea - ven cry Je - sus is Lord!
Yet gave his life a ran - som thus set - ting us free.
To show by works of pow - er that Je - sus is Lord.

Refrain
Je - sus is Lord! Je - sus is Lord!

Praise him with 'Hal - le - lu - jahs' for Je - sus is Lord!

83. The joy of the Lord

Alliene G. Vale
Arr. Betty Pulkingham
Brightly
E
B7
1. The joy of the Lord is my strength; the joy of the Lord is my strength; the joy of the Lord is my strength; the joy of the Lord is my strength.
2. If you want joy you must sing for it; if you want joy you must shout for it; if you want joy you must jump for it; the joy of the Lord is my strength.
3. The word of faith is nigh thee, even in thy mouth; the word of faith is nigh thee, even in thy mouth; the word of faith is nigh thee, even in thy mouth; the joy of the Lord is my strength.
A
E
B7
E
A-

B7
- ha ha ha ha ha ha ha ha ha ha. A-
E
- ha ha ha ha ha ha ha ha ha ha. A-
A
- ha ha ha ha ha ha ha ha ha ha. The
E
B7
E
joy of the Lord is my strength.

84. I heard the Lord

Capo 3(D)

With a delicate swing

Jacob Krieger
Arr. Betty Pulkingham

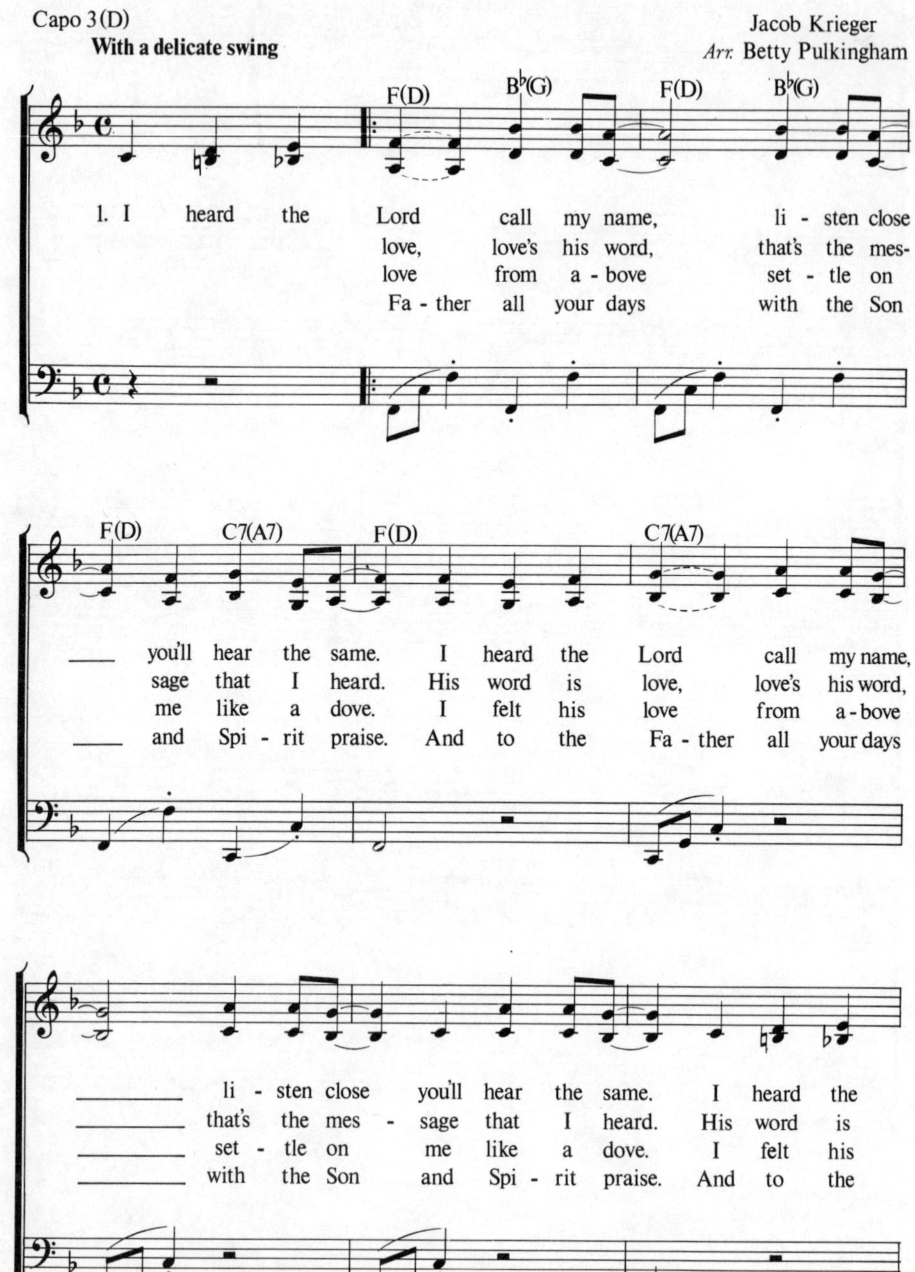

F(D) B♭(G) F(D) B♭(G)
1. I heard the Lord call my name, li - sten close
love, love's his word, that's the mes-
love from a - bove set - tle on
Fa - ther all your days with the Son
F(D) C7(A7) F(D) C7(A7)
you'll hear the same. I heard the Lord call my name,
sage that I heard. His word is love, love's his word,
me like a dove. I felt his love from a - bove
and Spi - rit praise. And to the Fa - ther all your days
li - sten close you'll hear the same. I heard the
that's the mes - sage that I heard. His word is
set - tle on me like a dove. I felt his
with the Son and Spi - rit praise. And to the

F(D)
B♭(G)
F(D)
B♭(G)
F(D)
C7(A7)
Lord call my name, li - sten close you'll hear the same.
love, love's his word, that's the mes - sage that I heard.
love from a - bove set - tle on me like a dove.
Fa - ther all your days with the Son and Spi - rit praise.
F(D)
C7(A7)
F(D)
1.-4. Take his hand, we are glo - ry bound.
1. Vs. 1, 3
2. Vs. 2, 4
Fine
A(F♯)
Dm (Bm)
2. His word is
4. And to the
Place your hand in his and you will
G(E)
G7(E7)
C(A)
know, he will show you where to go.
3. I felt his
1. I heard the

85. And can it be?

Charles Wesley

'Sagina'
Thomas Campbell

Thoughtfully, not too slow

1. And can it be that I should gain An
2. 'Tis mys - t'ry all! th'im - mor - tal dies! Who
3. He left his fa - ther's throne a - bove, So

in - t'rest in the Sav - iour's blood?
can ex - plore his strange de - sign ?
free, so in - fin - nite his grace ;

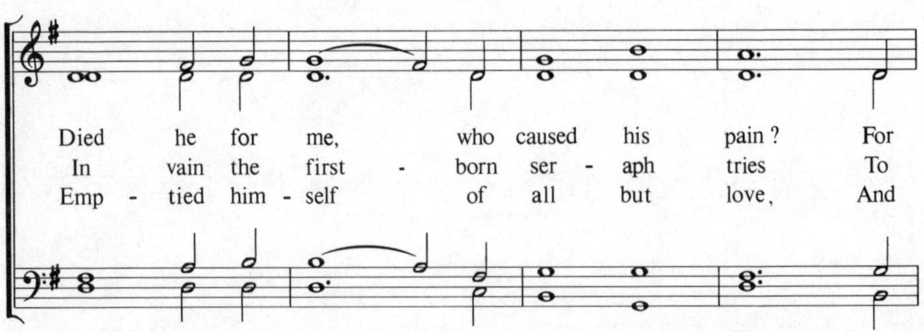
Died he for me, who caused his pain ? For
In vain the first - born ser - aph tries To
Emp - tied him - self of all but love, And

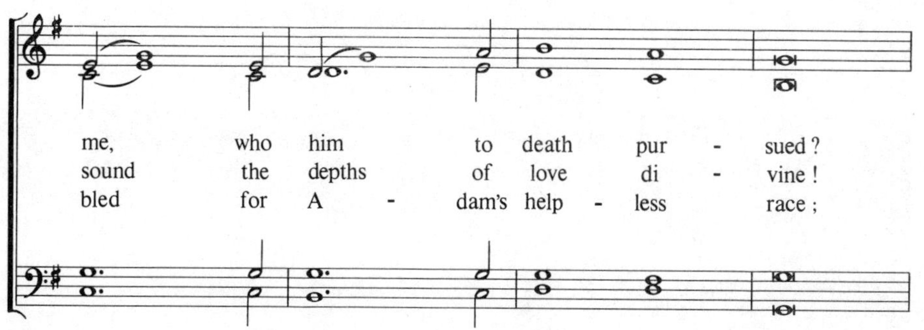
me, who him to death pur - sued?
sound the depths of love di - vine!
bled for A - dam's help - less race;

A - maz - ing love! how can it be That
'Tis mer - cy all! let earth a - dore, Let
'Tis mer - cy all, im - mense and free; For,

A-
thou, my God, shouldst die for me?
an - gel minds in - quire no more.
O my God, it found out me.

-maz - ing love! how can it be That
A - maz - ing love! how can it be
'Tis mer - cy all! let earth a - dore,
'Tis mer - cy all, im - mense and free;

thou, my God, shouldst die for me?
That thou my God, shouldst die for me?
Let an - gel minds in - quire no more.
For, O my God, it found out me.

4 Long my imprisoned spirit lay
Fast bound in sin and nature's night;
Thine eye diffused a quickening ray,
I woke, the dungeon flamed with light;
My chains fell off, my heart was free;
I rose, went forth, and followed thee.

5 No condemnation now I dread;
Jesus and all in him, is mine!
Alive in him, my living head,
And clothed in righteousness divine,
Bold I approach the eternal throne,
And claim the crown, through Christ my own.

go forth!

songs of outreach

86. Alleluia! Sons of God, arise!

Mimi Farra
Triumphantly
Refrain
C F C
Al - le - lu - ia! Al - le - lu - ia! Al – le – lu – ia, sons of
G C F
God, a - rise. Al – le – lu – ia! Al – le – lu – ia!
C G G7 C
Fine
sons of God, a – rise and fol – low the Lord.
G D7 G
Verses
1. Come and be clothed in his right – eous – ness; Come join the
2. Look at the world which is bound by sin; Walk in – to the
V. 1. only
V. 2. only
D7 G G7
Refrain
band who are called by his name.
midst of it pro – claim – ing my life.

87. Come and go with me

Anon.
Arr. Jeanne Harper

With a happy, light sound
E
A
E
1. Come and go with me ___ to my Fa-ther's house,
B7
E
to my Fa-ther's house, to my Fa-ther's house.
A
E
Come and go with me ___ to my Fa-ther's house where there's
B7
E
joy, ___ joy, ___ joy. ___

2. It's not very far to my Father's house…
3. There is room for all in my Father's house…
4. Everything is free in my Father's house…
5. Jesus is the way to my Father's house…
6. Jesus is the light in my Father's house…

Other verses may be added spontaneously, such as 'We will clap our hands' -- 'There is liberty' -- 'We will praise the Lord' etc., ending with 'Come and go with me.'

88. Ho! everyone that thirsteth

Adapted from Isaiah 55:1-2

Betty Pulkingham

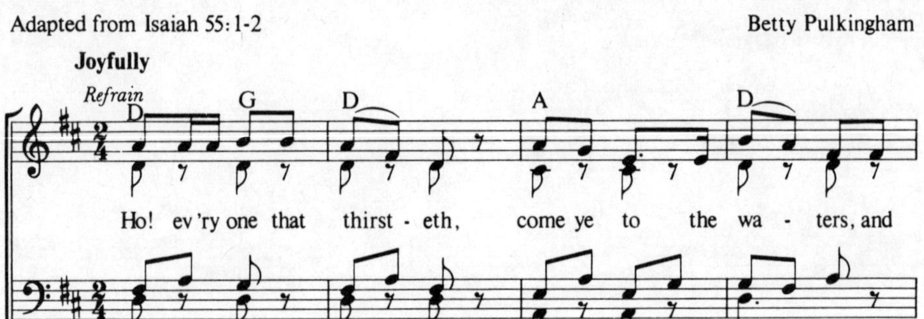

Joyfully
Refrain
D G D A D
Ho! ev'ry one that thirst - eth, come ye to the wa - ters, and

D G D A D
final ending
D
he that hath no mon - ey, come ye, buy and eat. eat.

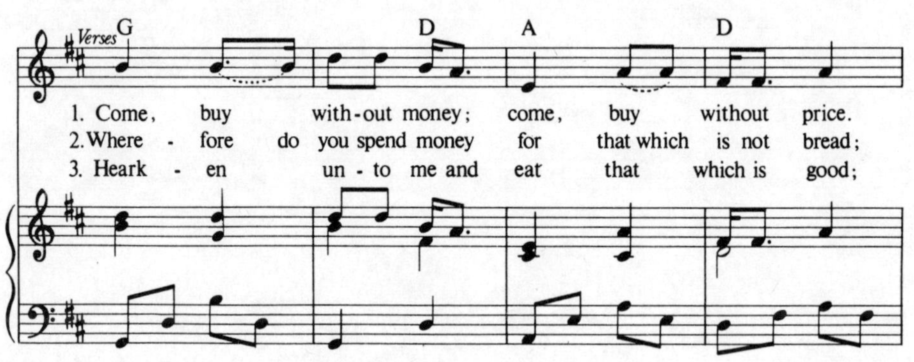

Verses
G D A D
1. Come, buy with-out money; come, buy without price.
2. Where - fore do you spend money for that which is not bread;
3. Heark - en un - to me and eat that which is good;

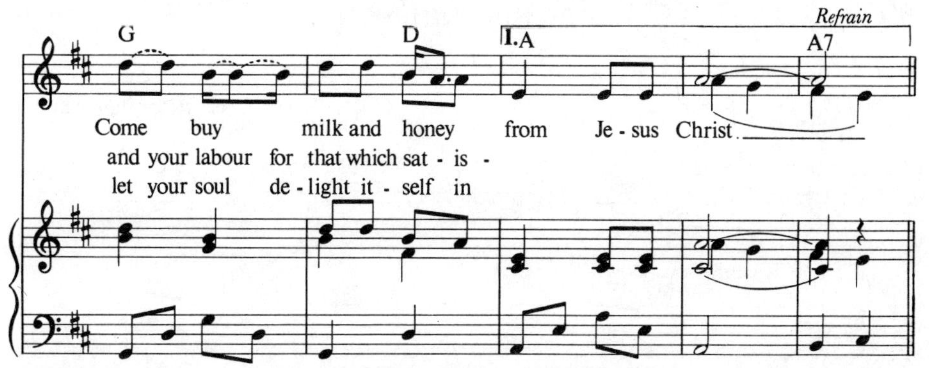
Refrain
G
D
1.A
A7
Come buy milk and honey from Je - sus Christ.
and your labour for that which sat - is -
let your soul de - light it - self in

Refrain
2.A
A7
3.A
A7
Refrain
fi - eth not?
fat - - ness, fat-ness, fat-ness.

89. The sea walker

Anon.
Arr. Betty Pulkingham

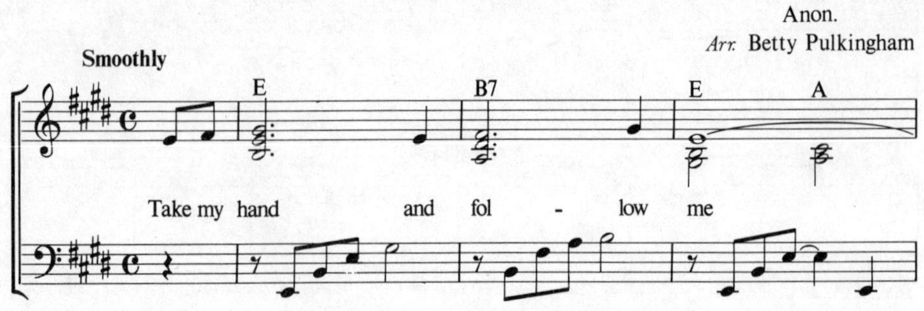
Smoothly
E
B7
E
A
Take my hand and fol - low me

E
Briskly
E
to see the sea walker, the

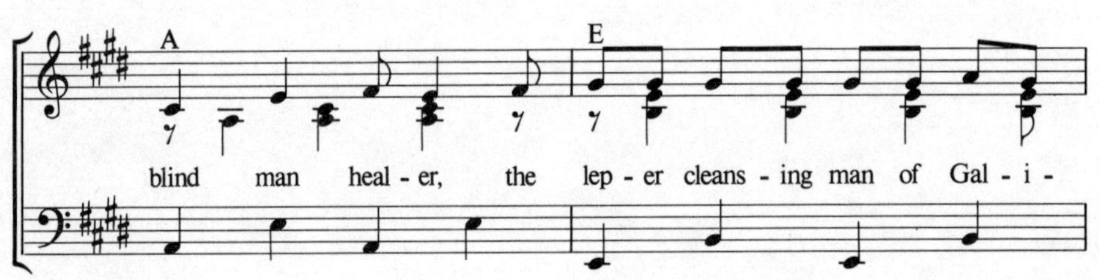
A
E
blind man heal - er, the lep - er cleans - ing man of Gal - i -

B7
E
E7
lee. He's the soul sav - er, the

A
E
B7
one who set me free, take my hand and fol - low

1.
final ending
E
A
E
E
A
E
me ______ to see the me.

90. O Lord, all the world belongs to you

Capo 3 (D)

Patrick Appleford
Arr. Jeanne Harper

Smoothly

F(D) C7(A7) F(D) B♭(G) D7(B7)

1. O Lord, all the world be - longs to you, and
2. The world's on - ly lov - ing to its friends, but
3. This world lives di - vid - ed and a - part; you

Gm(Em) D7(B7) Gm(Em) G(E) C(A) C7(A7)

you are al - ways mak - ing all things new. What is
your way of lov - ing ne - ver ends; lov - ing
draw men to - ge - ther and we start in your

F(D) A(F♯) Dm(Bm) D7(B7) Gm(Em) D7(B7)
wrong you for - give, and the new life you give is what's
en - em - ies too, and this lov - ing with you is what's
bo - dy to see that in fel - low - ship we can be
F(D) C7(A7) F(D) B♭(G) F(D)
turn-ing the world up - side down.
turn-ing the world up - side down.
turn-ing the world up - side down.

4. The world wants the wealth to live in state,
But you show a new way to be great:
Like a servant you came,
And if we do the same,
We'll be turning the world upside down.

5. O Lord, all the world belongs to you,
And you are always making all things new,
Send your Spirit on all
In your Church whom you call
To be turning the world upside down.

91. Peace is flowing

Anon.
Arr: Betty Pulkingham

Smoothly
E
B7
E
B7
E
Peace is flow-ing like a riv - er,
Flow - ing out through you and me, Spread - ing out in-to the
des - ert, Set - ting all the cap-tives free.

Other verses may be added:

Love is flowing ... Joy, Faith, Hope, *etc.*

Optional descant (for 3rd. verse onwards)

92. God is working his purpose out

Arthur Ainger
'Purpose'
Martin Shaw
With breadth
1. God is work - ing his pur - pose out As
2. From ut - most east to ut - most west, Wher -
3. March we forth in the strength of God, With the
4. All we can do is noth - ing worth Un -
year suc - ceeds to year: God is work - ing his
e'er man's foot hath trod, By the mouth of ma - ny
ban-ner of Christ un - furled, That the light of the glo - rious
less God bless-es the deed; Vain - ly we hope for the
pur - pose out, And the time is draw - ing near;
mes - sen - gers Goes forth the voice of God;
gos - pel of truth May shine through-out the world;
har - vest - tide Till God gives life to the seed; Yet

From 'Enlarged Songs of Praise' by permission Oxford University Press.

Near - er and near - er draws the time, The time that shall sure - ly
Give ear to me, ye con - ti - nents, Ye isles, give ear to
Fight we the fight with sor-row and sin To set their cap - tives
near - er and near - er draws the time, The time that shall sure - ly
be, When the earth shall be filled with the glo - ry of God As the
me, That the earth may be filled with the glo - ry of God As the
free, That the earth may be filled with the glo - ry of God As the
be, When the earth shall be filled with the glo - ry of God As the
Vs. 1, 2, 3.
V. 4.
wa - ters cov - er the sea.
wa - ters cov - er the sea.
wa - ters cov - er the sea.
wa - ters cov - er the sea.
f

The third stanza may be sung very effectively as a canon, with male voices beginning, treble voices following behind. (See left hand piano part.)

93. Go tell everyone

Alan Dale

Hubert Richards
Adapted by Betty Pulkingham

Freely
Am
Verse
Am
1. God's spi - rit is in my
Dm
Am
heart, he has called me and set me a - part.
E
Am
E7
This is what I have to do, what I have to
Brightly
A
Refrain
E7
do: He sent me to give the good news to the
A
E7
poor, tell prisoners that they are prisoners no more; tell

A D B7
blind peo - ple that they can see, and set the
E E7 A
down-trod - den free. And go tell
D E7 A
ev - 'ry - one the news that the king-dom of God has
A7 D
come, and go tell ev - 'ry - one the
Fine
E7 A E7 A
news that God's king-dom has come.

2. Just as the Father sent me
So I'm sending you out to be
My witness throughout the world
The whole of the world

3. Don't carry a load in your pack,
You don't need two shirts on your back,
A workman can earn his own keep
Can earn his own keep.

4. Don't worry what you have to say,
Don't worry because on that day
God's spirit will speak in your heart,
Will speak in your heart.

94. O Zion, haste

Mary Ann Thompson

'Tidings'
James Walch

Sturdily

1. O Zi - on, haste, thy mis - sion high ful - fill - ing,
2. Pro - claim to ev - 'ry peo - ple, tongue, and na - tion
3. Give of thy sons to bear the mes - sage glo - rious;

To tell to all the world that God is light;
That God, in whom they live and move, is love;
Give of thy wealth to speed them on their way;

That he who made all na - tions is not will - ing
Tell how he stooped to save his lost cre - a - tion,
Pour out thy soul for them in prayer vic - to - rious

One soul should per - ish, lost in shades of night:
And died on earth that man might live a - bove.
Till God shall bring his king-dom's joy - ful day.
Refrain
Pub - lish glad ti - dings: ti - dings of peace,
ti - dings of Je - sus, re - demp - tion and re - lease.

4. He comes again! O Zion, ere thou meet him,
Make known to every heart his saving grace;
Let none whom he hath ransomed fail to greet him,
Through thy neglect, unfit to see his face.
Refrain

95. God has spoken

'Song of good news'

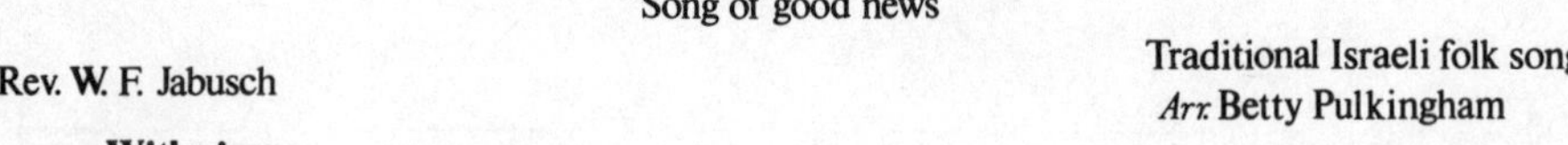
Rev. W. F. Jabusch
Traditional Israeli folk song
Arr. Betty Pulkingham
With vigor

Refrain
Am
E
God has spo - ken to his peo - ple, hal - le - lu - jah!

Am
And his words are words of wis - dom, ha - le - lu - jah!

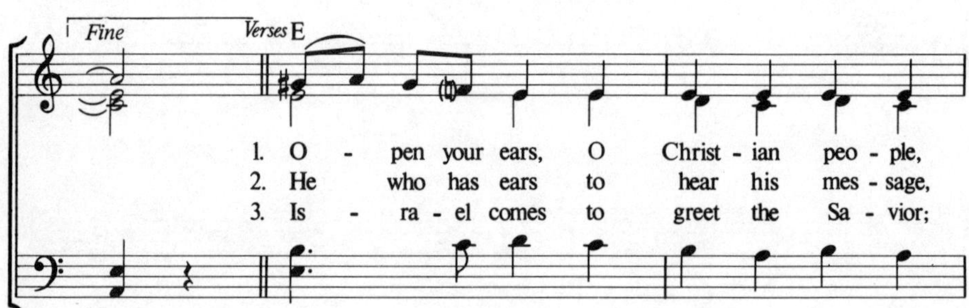
Fine
Verses E
1. O - pen your ears, O Christ - ian peo - ple,
2. He who has ears to hear his mes - sage,
3. Is - ra - el comes to greet the Sa - vior;

E
O - pen your ears and hear good news. O - pen your hearts, O
He who has ears, then let him hear. He who would learn the
Ju - dah is glad to see his day. From east and west the

Dm
E
Refrain
roy - al priest-hood, God has come to you.
way of wis - dom, let him hear God's word.
peo - ples tra - vel, He will show the way.

The final refrain may be repeated several times as a round, the second part beginning at ✱ For additional variety, verses may be sung alternately by male and treble voices.

96. Go forth and tell

Capo 1 (E)

J.E. Seddon

M.A. Baughen

Boldly, with a swing

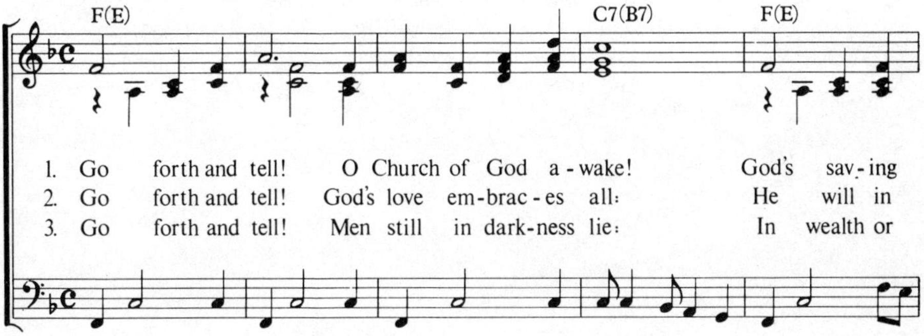

F(E) C7(B7) F(E)

1. Go forth and tell! O Church of God a - wake! God's sav - ing
2. Go forth and tell! God's love em-brac - es all: He will in
3. Go forth and tell! Men still in dark-ness lie: In wealth or

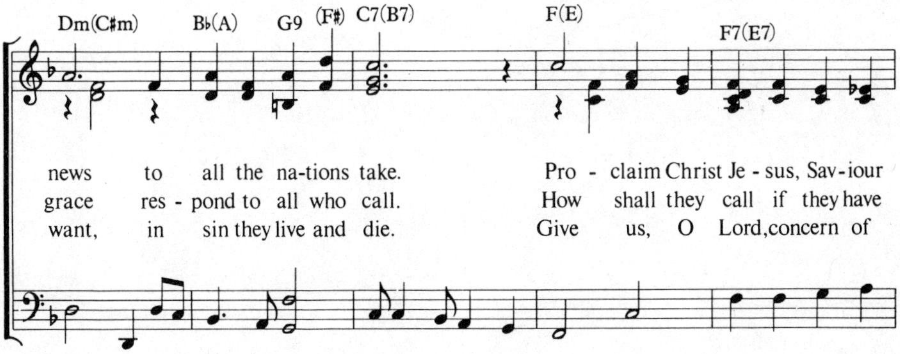

Dm(C#m) B♭(A) G9 (F#) C7(B7) F(E) F7(E7)

news to all the na-tions take. Pro - claim Christ Je - sus, Sav-iour
grace res - pond to all who call. How shall they call if they have
want, in sin they live and die. Give us, O Lord, concern of

Bb(A)
F(E)
C7(B7)
F(E)
Lord, and King, that all the world his wor-thy praise may sing.
ne - ver heard the gra-cious in - vit - ta - tion of his word.
heart and mind, a love like thine which cares for all man - kind.

4. Go forth and tell! The doors are open wide:
Share God's good gifts with men so long denied.
Live out your life as Christ, your Lord, shall choose,
Your ransomed powers for his sole glory use.

5. Go forth and tell! O Church of God, arise:
Go in the strength which Christ your Lord supplies.
Go, till all nations his great name adore
And serve him Lord and King for evermore.

Sing a psalm!

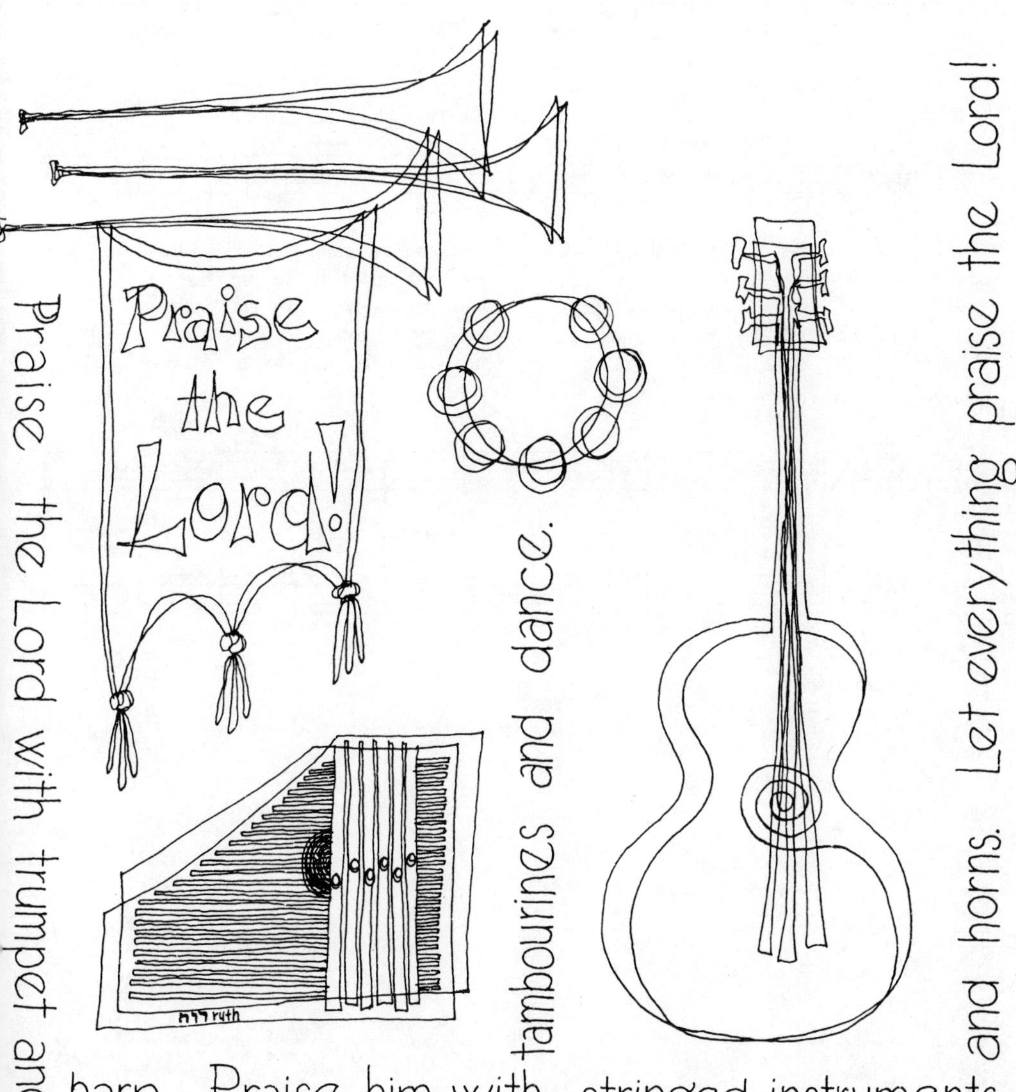
Praise the Lord!
Praise the Lord with trumpet and harp. Praise him with tambourines and dance. Praise him with stringed instruments and horns. Let everything praise the Lord!
ruth

97. Joy in the Lord

(Psalm 100)

Jane Trigg
Arr. Betty Pulkingham

With a light bounce
Refrain
D A D A D G A7
Fine
S
A
T
B
Joy in the Lord, O be joy - ful in the Lord, all ___ ye lands.
(all)

G D G E7 A A7

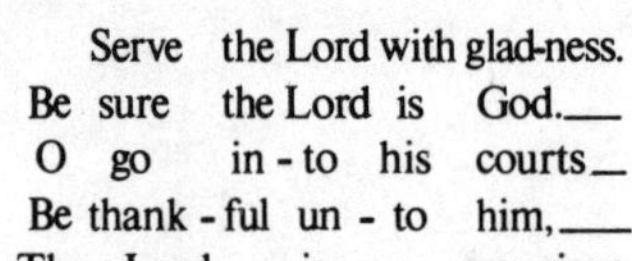
Serve the Lord with glad-ness. Come be - fore him with a song.
Be sure the Lord is God.___ He has made us, we are his.
O go in - to his courts___ with thanks-giv - ing and praise.
Be thank - ful un - to him,___ and speak good of his name.
The Lord is gra-cious, mer - ci - ful for ev - er - more.

98. Behold, how good and how pleasant it is

(Psalm 133)

Capo 3 (A)

Kathleen Thomerson
Arr. Betty Pulkingham

Calypso style

C(A)
F(D)
C(A)
Be - hold how good and how plea - sant it
G(E)
C(A)
F(D)
is for breth - ren to dwell to-geth - er in
B♭(G)
F(D)
G(E)
C(A)
u - ni - ty.
1. It. is like
2. As the dew
3. For there

Gm7 (Em7)
C(A)
the pre - cious oint - ment up - on the head that ran
of Her - mon and as the dew that de -
the Lord com - mand - ed, com -
F(D)
C(A)
down up - on the beard, even Aaron's
scend - ed up - on the moun - tains of Zi - on,
mand - - - ed the bless - ing.
verse 3
B♭(G)
B♭M7(GM7)
G7(E7)
beard, that ran down to the skirts of his gar - ments;
For there the Lord com - mand - ed the
Ev - en

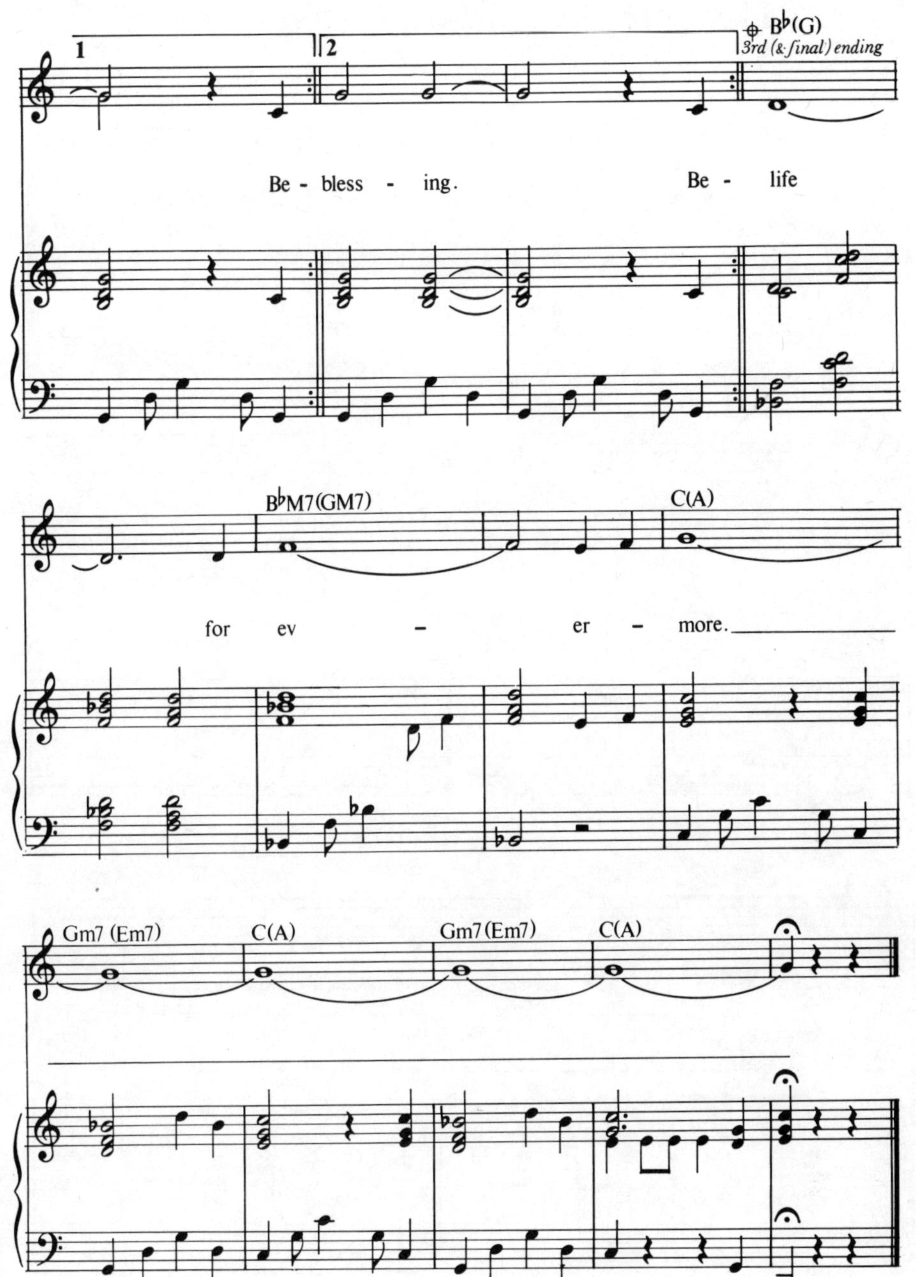
1
2
Bb(G)
3rd (& final) ending
Be - bless - ing.
Be - life
BbM7(GM7)
C(A)
for ev - er - more.
Gm7 (Em7)
C(A)
Gm7(Em7)
C(A)

99. The Lord has done great things for us

(Psalm 126)

Music by Eleven: fifty-nine
Arr. Betty Pulkingham

Soft rock
Introduction
1.
Verse
E
1. When the Lord re - stored the
said a - mong the
store our
goes forth
2.
Bm7
E
Verse 2 ⊕
for - tunes of Zi – on, we were like those who
na - tions, 'The Lord has done great things for
for - tunes, O Lord, as the wa - ter cours - es in the
weep - ing bear - ing the seed for

E
dream. Then our mouths were filled with
Ne - geb. May those who sow in
sow - ing, shall come home with shouts of
Bm7
E
laugh - ter, and our tongues with shouts of
tears, reap with shouts of
joy, bring - ing his sheaves
E
Refrain
joy!
them. The Lord has done great things for
joy!
with him.

D
E
us, and we are glad.
1.
2.
The Lord has done
2. Then they
3. Re -
4. He that
Final

100. The Lord hath put a new song

(Psalm 40)

Mimi Armstrong Farra

Joyfully
Refrain
D
G
D
The Lord hath put a new song in my
A
D
mouth, in my mouth, in my mouth. The
G
Lord hath put a new song in my mouth,
A
D
G
D
Fine
e – ven praise un – to our God.

G
Verses may be sung as solo
D
1. And ma-ny shall __ see it and fear and trust,
2. I de - light to do thy will, oh God, thy
3. I have not hid thy right-eous-ness with - in my heart, with-
4. I've not con - cealed thy lov - ing kind-ness and thy truth,
5. So let thy ___ lov - ing kind-ness and thy truth,
6. Let all those that seek thee re - joice and be glad, re-
A
D
fear and trust, fear and trust. And
will, oh God, thy will, oh God.
in my heart, with - in my heart. I
and thy truth, and thy truth, I've
and thy truth, and thy truth, so
joice and be glad, re - joice and be glad. Let

G D
ma - ny shall ___ see it and fear and trust,
I de - light to do thy will, oh God. Thy
have not hid thy right-eous-ness with - in my heart.
not con - cealed thy lov - ing kind-ness and thy_ truth,
let thy ___ lov - ing kind-ness and thy_ truth con-
all those that seek thee re - joice and be glad, re-
A A7 D G D Refrain
and shall trust in the Lord. ___
law is with - in my ___ heart. ___
I have de - clared thy sal - va - tion.
from the great con - gre - ga - tion.
tin - u - al - ly pre - serve me.
joice and be glad in ___ thee. ___
Refrain

101. As a doe

(Psalm 42)

Capo 2 (Am)

Mike Fitzgerald
Arr. Mimi Farra

Sustained, without dragging
Refrain
Bm(Am)
Em(Dm)
As a doe longs for run-ning
Bm(Am)
streams, so longs my soul for
F♯7(E7)
Bm(Am)
1,3
Verse
you, my God.
1. My soul is
3. Why so

Em(Dm)
thirst - ing for the God of life;
down - cast, O my soul?
Bm(Am)
F♯(E)
F♯7(E7)
when shall I see him face to face?
Why do you sigh so deep with - in?
Bm(Am)
Em(Dm)
I have no food but tears day and
Place your hope in the God of

Bm(Am)
F♯7(E7)
Bm(Am)
night; and men say, 'Where is your God?'
life. I shall praise him a - gain.
Refrain
2,4
G(F)
2. I re - mem-ber and my
4. When I find my soul
D(C)
G(F)
soul melts with - in. I'm on my
down - cast with - in, I think of

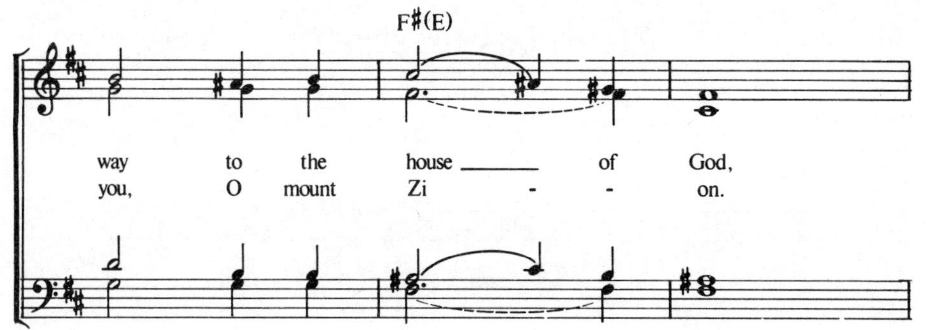
F♯(E)
way to the house ___ of God,
you, O mount Zi - - on.

G(F)
D(C)
a - mong cries ___ of joy ___ and praise;
Deep calls to deep as your wa - ters roar;

Bm(Am)
F♯7(E7)
Bm(Am)
Refrain
place ___ your trust ___ in God.
ov - er me all your waves pour.

102. The Lord's my shepherd

Psalm 23
Scottish Psalter

(Psalm 23)

Jessie Seymour Irvine
Arr. Thomas Pritchard
Descant Betty Pulkingham

Flowing

Descant
2. My soul he doth
4. My ta - ble thou hast
1. The Lord's my shep - herd, I'll not
2. My soul he doth re - store a -
3. Yea, though I walk in death's dark

re-store a-gain And me to walk doth make
fur-nish-ed In pre-sence of my foes.
want; He makes me down to lie In
gain; And me to walk doth make With -
vale, Yet will I fear none ill: For

The paths of right-eous-ness, e'en for
My head thou dost with oil a - noint
pas - tures green; he lead - eth me The
in the paths of right - eous - ness, E'en
thou art with me; and thy rod And

his own name's sake.
and my cup o - ver - flows.
qui - et wa - ters by.
for his own name's sake.
staff me com - fort still.

4. My table thou hast furnished
   In presence of my foes;
   My head thou dost with oil anoint,
   And my cup overflows.

5. Goodness and mercy all my life
   Shall surely follow me:
   And in God's house for evermore
   My dwelling-place shall be.

103. Sing a new song to the Lord

Timothy Dudley-Smith
(Psalm 98)
David G. Wilson
With a swing
G F G F
1. Sing a new song to the Lord,
2. Now to the ends of the earth
3. Sing a new song and re - joice,
G Dm G F
He to whom won - ders be - long! Re -
See his sal - va - tion is shown! And
Pub - lish his prai - ses a - broad! Let
Em A
joice in his tri - umph and
still he re - mem - bers his
voi - ces in chor - us, with
Em F D7
tell of his power, O
mer - cy and truth, Un -
trum - pet and horn, Re -

G Dm7 Am D7
sing to the Lord a new
chang - ing in love to his
sound for the joy of the
G Am7 G Am7 G
1-3. 4.
song!
own.
Lord!

4. Join with the hills and the sea
   Thunders of praise to prolong!
In judgement and justice he comes to the earth,
   O sing to the Lord a new song!

104. Bless thou the Lord

(Psalm 103)

Betty Pulkingham

Smoothly
D Refrain
Bless thou the Lord, O my soul,
bless thou the Lord, O my soul.
A
D
Bless thou the Lord,
O my soul, and for - get not all his ben - e -
A
D
1-5
fits.
1. Who for -
2. Who re -
3. The
D
final ending
fits.

G
Verses
D
giv - eth all thine in - i - qui-ties, who
deem - eth thy life from de - struc - tion, who
Lord is mer - ci - ful and gra - cious, slow to
A7
D
A7
heal - eth all thy dis - eas - es.
crown - eth thee with lov - ing kind - ness.
an - ger and plen - teous in mer - cy.

4. For as the heaven is high above the earth,
   So great his mercy toward them that fear him.

5. Like as a father pitieth his children,
   So the Lord pitieth them that fear him.

105. I rejoiced when I heard them say

(Psalm 122)

Betty Pulkingham

Joyfully
A Refrain
D
I re - joiced when I heard them say,
E
A
'Let us go to God's house to - day!' I re-joiced when I
D
E
A
last time
heard them say, 'Let us go to God's house.'

D
A
1. And now our
2. Je - ru - sa - lem is
3. For the peace of Je -
4. For love of my
E7
A
feet are stand - ing, stand - ing with -
built as a ci - ty, it is
ru - - sa - lem pray, peace be to your
breth - - ren and friends, for love of the
D
A
in thy gates, O Je -
there that the tribes go up, the
homes, peace to your
house of the Lord, I will say,

E7
A
Refrain
ru - - - sa - lem.
tribes of the Lord.
homes al - way.
Peace, peace up - on you.'
E
A
E
Let us go to God's house. Let us go
E7
A
A
to God's house.

come as children

songs for children of all ages

106. The butterfly song

Brian Howard

Playfully

D
G
1. If I were a but - ter - fly, I'd thank you, Lord, for
2. If I were an e - le - phant, I'd thank you, Lord, by
3. If I were a wig - gily worm, I'd thank you, Lord, that
D
giv - ing me wings. And if I were a ro - bin in a tree, I'd
rais - ing my trunk. And if I were a kan - ga - roo, you
I could squirm. And if I were a bil - ly - goat, I'd
A
A7
D
thank you, Lord, that I could sing. And if I were a
know I'd hop right up to you. And if I were an
thank you, Lord, for my strong throat. And if I were a
G
fish in the sea, I'd wig - gle my tail and I'd
oct - o - pus, I'd thank you, Lord, for
fuz - zy - wuz - zy bear, I'd thank you, Lord, for my

A
gig - gle with glee, but
my fine looks, but
fuz - zy-wuz-zy hair, but
I just thank you, Fa-ther, for mak - ing me
D G D
'me.' For you gave me a heart and you
G
gave me a smile. You gave me Je - sus and you made me your child. And
A D G D
I just thank you, Fa-ther, for mak-ing me 'me.'

A good song to stimulate a child's imagination. Verse 3 was added by children from a multi-racial, inner-city school.

107. Jesus, Jesus is my Lord

John Franklin *(age 12)* Betty Pulkingham

Cheerfully
Refrain
C F C G G7 C
Fine
Verses
1 2
Je - sus, Je - sus is my Lord; al-ways o-bey what Je - sus says.
Je - sus says.
1. That's the way to lay down your life,
2. He re - wards you, mak-ing you free,
3. He has giv-en his Spi-rit to you,
al-ways o - bey what Je - sus says.
The ones who come for Je - sus' life
And then you have pow-er ov-er the en - e - my,
So keep his words and he will keep you,
al-ways o-bey what Je - sus says.
Refrain

108. The Lord is my shepherd

(2-part round)

Adapted from Psalm 23
Capo 1 (E)

Anon.
Arr. Betty Pulkingham

Smoothly flowing
1
F(E)
C7(B7)
F(E)
The Lord is my Shep - herd, I'll fol - low him al - way, He
leads me by still wa - ters, I'll fol - low him al - way. Al -
2
way, al - way, I'll fol - low him al - way. Al - way, al -
Lord is my Shep - herd, I'll fol - low him al - way. He leads me by still
way, I'll fol - low him al - way, The
wa - ter, I'll fol - low him al - Al - way.

109. Oh, how I love Jesus

Capo 1 (E)

Refrain: F. Whitfield
Arr. Betty Pulkingham

With simplicity

F(E)
B♭(A) F(E)
(Question) Hey, (name) do you love Je - sus? (Answer) Yes, I love
B♭(A) F(E)
C7(B7)
Je - sus. (Q)Are you sure you love Je - sus?(A)Yes, I'm sure I love
F(E)
B♭(A) F(E)
Je - sus.(Q)Tell me, why do you love Je - sus?(A)This is why I love
B♭(A) F(E)
Gm (F♯m)
C7(B7)
F(E)
Je - sus,(All) be - cause he first loved me, Yes, I

B♭(A) F(E)
B♭(A) F(E)
Refrain:
F(E)
love him, this is why I love him. Oh,
C7 (B7)
how I love Je - sus, Oh,
F(E)
F(E)
how I love Je - sus, Oh,
Gm (F♯m)
how I love Je - sus, be - cause he

C 7(B7)
1. F(E)
B♭(A)
F(E)
first loved me. Yes, I love him, this is
B♭(A) F(E)
2. F(E)
why I love him. Hey, me.

The first part of this song is a dialogue. One person starts it and the one who is named sings the answers, and in turn asks the questions the second time round.
A good concluding verse is 'Hey saints' (or 'family' or 'kids') - - - some term which includes all of those present.

110. Praise the Lord

"Sing, sing, praise and sing"

Elizabeth Syré

With a swing

Refrain
F
C7
F
Sing, sing, praise and sing! Hon - our God for ev - ery - thing.

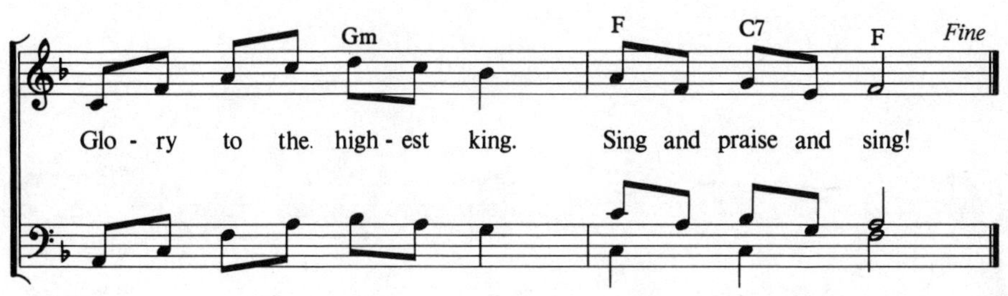

Gm
F
C7
F
Fine
Glo - ry to the high - est king. Sing and praise and sing!

Verses
C
F
G7
C
C7
D.C.
1. Clap your hands, lift your voice, praise the Lord and re - joice!
2. Full of joy, full of rest, in our Lord we are blessed.
3. Are you weak? Ne - ver mind! Come and sing, "God is kind!"

4. Love and peace is so near.
   Praise the Lord!
   God can hear!

5. Cymbal, harp, violin,
   Angels, priests,
   All join in.

111. The body song

Adapted from I Cor. 12. 14-26

Betty Pulkingham

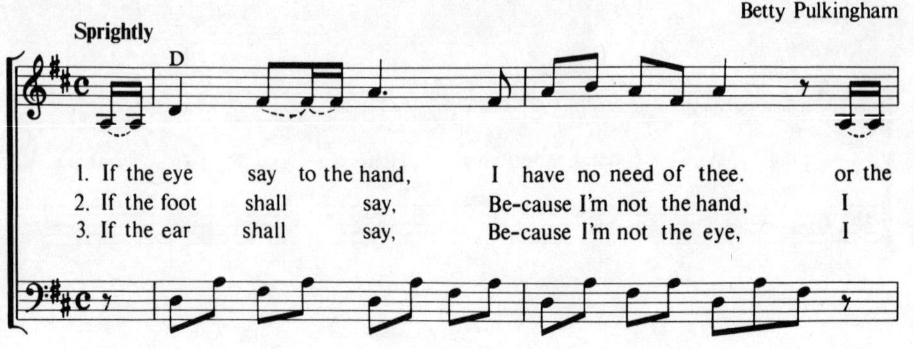
Sprightly
D
1. If the eye say to the hand, I have no need of thee. or the
2. If the foot shall say, Be-cause I'm not the hand, I
3. If the ear shall say, Be-cause I'm not the eye, I

A
head to the feet, I have no need of you. Well, oh
don't feel like a handsome part. Well, oh
don't seem to see things ve - ry clear - - - ly. Well, oh

D
how can we write or hold a thim-ble? How can we walk or run so nim-ble?
what does it matter to be first or to be latter? God has
where were the hearing, and oh where were the smelling if the

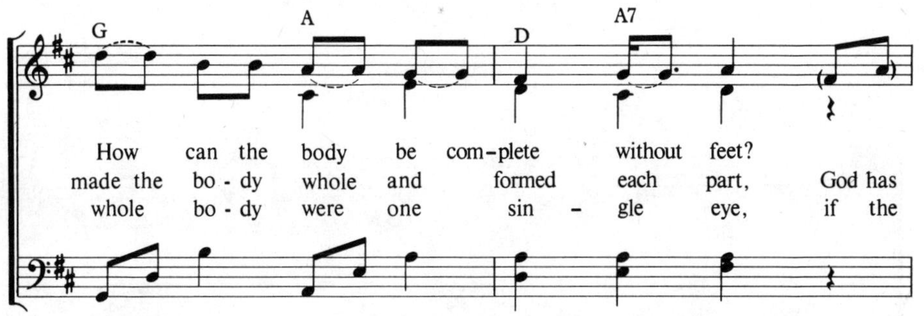
G
A
D
A7
How can the body be com-plete without feet?
made the bo - dy whole and formed each part, God has
whole bo - dy were one sin - gle eye, if the

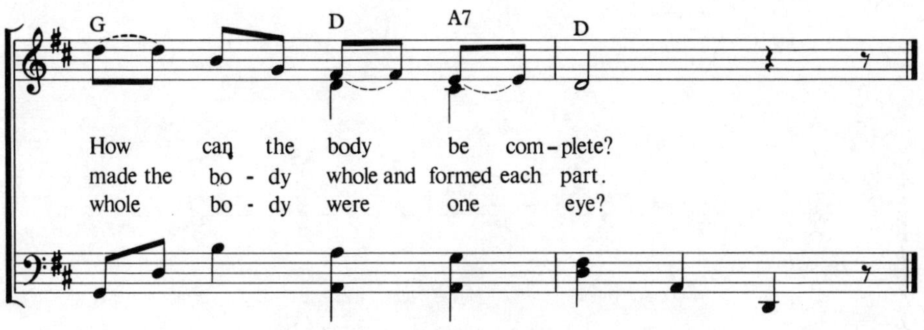
G
D
A7
D
How can the body be com-plete?
made the bo - dy whole and formed each part.
whole bo - dy were one eye?

4. One / single 'I', it cannot be a body.
   One / single 'you' a body? 'Nay!'
 Oh,/God hath set the members,
   They are / many, many members,
 Yet one / body as it pleased him are they.
   Yet one / body as it pleased him are they.

This is a good action song: point to the eye, the hand, etc. as they are mentioned.

112. We love the Lord

'David's song'

David Pulkingham
(Age 4)

Slowly and quietly

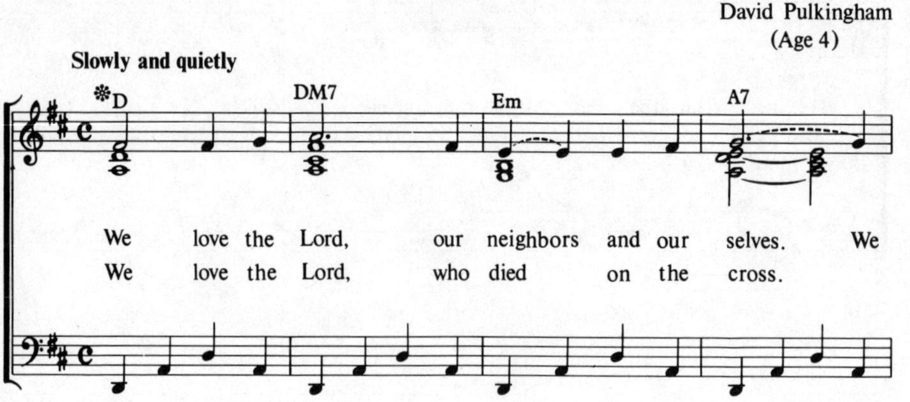

D
DM7
Em
A7
We love the Lord, our neighbors and our selves. We
We love the Lord, who died on the cross.

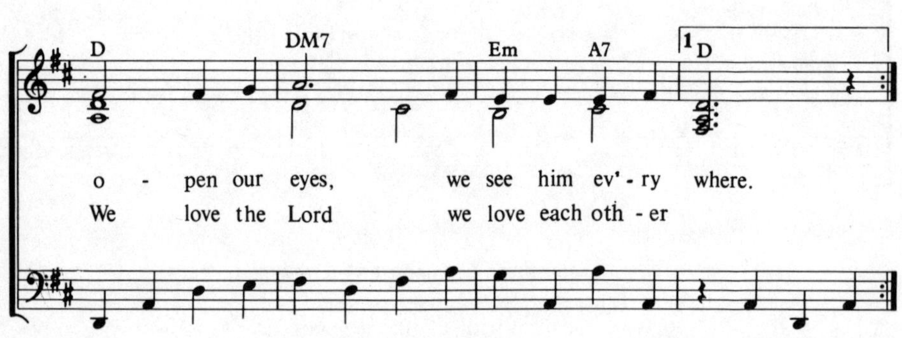

D
DM7
Em
A7
1 D
o - pen our eyes, we see him ev'-ry where.
We love the Lord we love each oth - er

2 D
DM7
Em
too. We o - pen our eyes, we see Je - sus

A7
D
DM7
Em
Christ; he looks down at us, we look up at

A7
D
DM7
Em
A7
D
him. We trust in him e - ter - nal - ly.

❉Children of all ages enjoy singing this song with graceful and simple motions: 'We' (hands pointing to self) 'love the Lord' (hands lifted up), 'our neighbors' (hands circling outwards) 'and ourselves' (back to self). 'We open our eyes' (hands over eyes, then opening like gates swinging open), 'we see him everywhere' (same as 'neighbors'). 'We love the Lord' (as above) 'who died on the cross' (forearms crossed). 'We love the Lord' (as above) 'to love each other too' (same as 'neighbors'). 'We open our eyes' (repeat above), 'we see Jesus Christ' (looking up), 'he looks down at us' (looking and extending arms down), 'we look up at him' (looking and extending arms up). 'We trust in him eternally' (arms in encircling motion).

113. Thank you, Lord

Capo 1(E)

Diane Davis

Bouncy

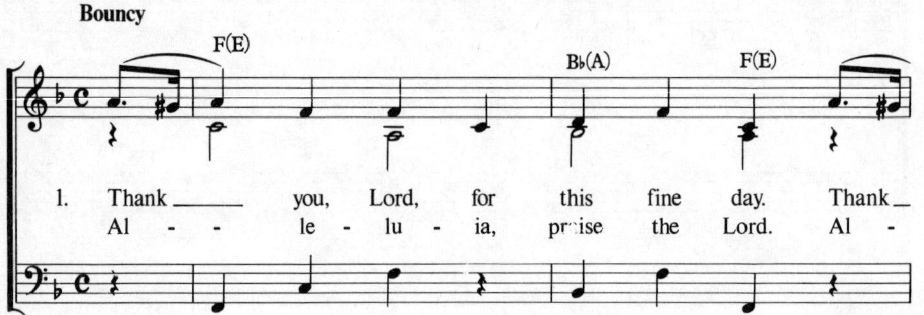

F(E)
Bb(A)
F(E)
1. Thank you, Lord, for this fine day. Thank
Al - - le - lu - ia, praise the Lord. Al -

C7(B7)
F(E)
you, Lord, for this fine day. Thank you, Lord, for
- le - lu - ia, praise the Lord. Al - - le - lu - ia,

Bb(A)
F(E)
Bb(A)
C7(B7)
F(E)
this fine day, Right where we are.
praise the Lord, Right where we are.

2. Thank you, Lord, for loving us.
3. Thank you, Lord, for giving us peace.
4. Thank you, Lord, for setting us free.
5. Thank you, Lord, for games to play.

114. Jesus is a friend of mine

Paul Mazak *(Age4)*
Arr. Betty Pulkingham

With childlike simplicity

E B7 E A B7
1. Je - sus is a friend of mine, praise
E B7 E B7
him. Praise him. Je - sus is a
E A B7 E
friend of mine, praise him.
rit.

2. Jesus died to set us free, praise him.

3. He gave us the victory, praise him.

4. Jesus is the King of kings, praise him.

115. The wedding banquet

Str. Miriam Therese Winter
Arr. Betty Pulkingham

Lively
Refrain
D
D7
G
I can - not come. I can - not come to the
D
A7
ban - quet, don't trou - ble me now. I have mar - ried a
D
D7
G
wife, I have bought me a cow. I have fields and com-
D
A7
- mitments that cost a pret - ty sum. Pray, hold me ex - cused, I can - not

'The wedding banquet' available on album AVS 101 from Avant Garde Records, Inc. 250 W. 57th St., N.Y., or 12 Portland Road, London, England.

Verses
G
1. A cer - tain man held a
come. 2. The mas - ter rose up in
3. When all the poor had as -
4. Now God has writ - ten a
D
Fine
D
feast on his fine es - tate in town, he
an - ger, called his ser - vants by name, said: "Go
- sem - bled, there was still room to spare, so the
les - son for the rest of man - kind; if
A
A7
D
laid a fes - tive ta - ble and wore a wed - ding
in - to the town, fetch the blind and the
mas - ter de - man - ded: "Go search ev - 'ry -
we're slow in res - pond - ing, he may leave us be -

D7
gown. He sent in - vi - ta - tions to his
lame, fetch the pea - sant and the pau - per, for
where, to the high - ways and the by - ways, and
hind. He's pre - par - ing a ban - quet for that
D
A
neigh - bors far and wide, but when the meal was
this I have willed, my ban - quet must be
force them to come in. My ta - ble must be
great and glo - rious day. When the Lord and Mas - ter
A7
D
Refrain
rea - dy, each of them re - plied:
crow - ded, and my ta - ble must be filled."
filled be - fore the ban - quet can be - gin."
calls us, be cer - tain not to say:
D.C.

songs for a season

116. Wake up!

Betty Pulkingham

Lightly and sprightly
Refrain
D
G
A7
Wake up! Wake up! It's time to rise and sing the praise of
A
Je - sus, al - le-lu, al - le - lu - ia. It's time to rise, to sing, to
F♯m
shout, to bring him all your heart. He'll do the big - ger
part, if you will on - ly make a start.
Fine

G D C D
verse 5
1. In the days of No - ah's fam - i - ly, the peo - ple didn't know what the score was e - ter - nal - ly. They ate, and drank, got mar - ried and then their
2. John came bap - tiz - ing in the wil - der - ness; preach - ing to those who their sins con - fessed. But to those who came for strife and de - bate, he said,
3. When Je - sus came to John in the wil - der - ness; John said, 'I should be the one to come to you, I must con - fess! For I bap - tize with wa - ter at the most, but
4. Je - sus told a sto - ry of ten mai - dens fair; five were wise and rea - dy, five did not pre - pare. Those girls had lamps, but oh, dear me! They
5. What good is a lamp with - out an - y oil? What good is our life if we strug - gle and toil, but,

G
D
C
D
Refrain
sons and their daughters did the same things a - gain.
'Who told you to come here, you tribe of snakes?'
you will bap - tize with the Ho - ly Ghost!'
had no oil to light them so that they could see.
G
verse 5
D
C
D
can - not see God's king - dom here, and
G
D
C
D
Refrain
live the loving life of his son so dear?

117. On Jordan's bank

Charles Coffin
Tr. John Chandler

Gary Miles
Arr. Betty Pulkingham

With vigor
A G A G D A D C G A G D A
final ending
1. On Jor-dan's bank the Bap-tist's cry An-noun-ces that the Lord is nigh; A-wake and heark-en, for he brings Glad ti-dings of the King of kings.
2. Then cleansed be ev-'ry breast from sin; Make straight the way for God with-in, And let each heart pre-pare a home Where such a mighty guest may come.
3. For thou art our sal-va-tion, Lord, Our re-fuge, and our great re-ward; With-out thy grace we waste a-way Like flowers that with-er and de-cay.

4. To heal the sick stretch out thine hand,
And bid the fallen sinner stand;
Shine forth, and let thy light restore
Earth's own true loveliness once more.

5. All praise, eternal Son, to thee,
Whose advent doth thy people free;
Whom with the Father we adore
And Holy Ghost for evermore.

118. Calypso carol

Michael Perry
Arr. Stephen Coates

Liltingly
D G A
1. See him a - ly - ing on a bed of straw;
2. Star of sil - ver sweep a - cross the skies,
3. An - gels, sing a - gain the song you sang,
A7 D
draugh - ty sta - ble with an op - en door,
show where Je - sus in the man - ger lies.
bring God's glo - ry to the heart of man;
D G Em
Ma - ry cra - dl - ing the babe she bore; The
Shep - herds swift - ly from your stu - por rise to
Sing that Bethl' - hem's lit - tle ba - by can
A7 D D7
prince of glo - ry is his name.
see the Sav - iour of the world.
be sal - va - tion to the soul.

Refrain:
G
D
Oh, now car - ry me to Beth - le - hem to
A7
D
see the Lord ap - pear to men;
B7
Em
Just as poor as was the sta - ble then, The
A7
Verses 1-3
Verse 4
D Gm D Gm D
prince of glo - ry when he came.

4. Mine are riches from thy poverty,
From thine innocence, eternity;
Mine, forgiveness by thy death for me,
Child of sorrow for my joy.

119. Oh, Mary, don't you weep

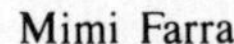

Mimi Farra

Gently rocking

Refrain Cm (Am)

Oh, ——— Ma - ry don't you weep ———

Fm (Dm) 1. Cm (Am)

and Ma-ry don't you cry. ———

2. Cm (Am) Gm(Em) Cm(Am) 3.4. Cm (Am) Gm(Em)

cry. ——— cry. ———

Cm(Am)

———

Fine

Cm(Am)
1. Oh, lit - tle ba - by Je - sus,
2. Ba - by Je - sus is gon - na die
3. Oh, sing glo - ry hal - le - lu - jah,

Fm (Dm)
Cm (Am)
Gm(Em)
Refrain
ba - by Je - sus is gon - na die, but
gon - na die that we might live for - ev - er.
glo - ry, glo - ry ba - by Je - sus.

120. See, amid the winter's snow

Edward Caswall
'Humility'
John Goss
Tenderly
Solo or unison
1. See, a - mid the win ter's snow, born for us on earth be - low, see the ten - der lamb ap-pears, prom - ised from e - ter - nal years.
2. Lo, with - in a man - ger lies he who built the star - ry skies, he who, throned in height sub-lime, sits a - mid the cher - u - bim.
3. Say, ye ho - ly shep - herds, say, what your joy - ful news to - day; where - fore have ye left your sheep on the lone - ly moun - tain steep?
Refrain
Hail, thou ev - er bless - ed morn! Hail re - demp - tion's hap - py dawn!

Sing through all Je - ru - sa-lem:
Christ is born in Beth - le - hem.

4. As we watched at dead of night,
   Lo, we saw a wondrous light:
Angels, singing peace on earth,
   Told us of the Saviour's birth.

5. Sacred infant, all divine,
   What a tender love was thine,
Thus to come from highest bliss
   Down to such a world as this!

6. Teach, O teach us, holy child,
   By thy face so meek and mild,
Teach us to resemble thee
   In thy sweet humility.

121. Go tell it on the mountain

North American spiritual
Arr. Betty Pulkingham

Flowing

Refrain
*G
CM7
G
Am
D7
Go tell it on the moun - tain, ov - er the hills and

G
D
G
CM7
G
ev - 'ry where. Go tell it on the moun - tain that

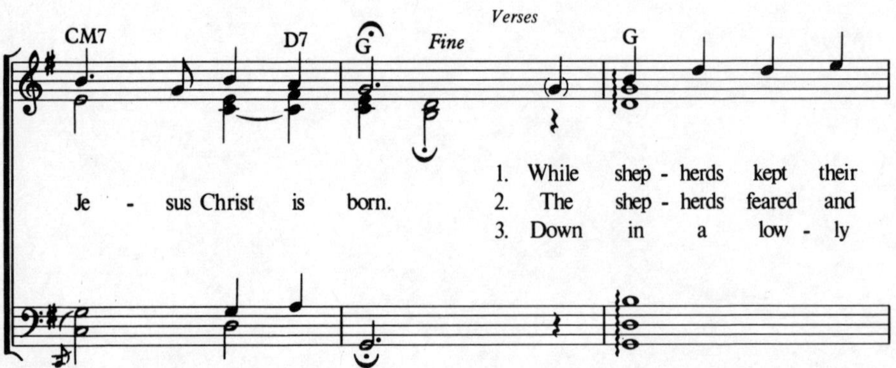
CM7
D7
G
Fine
Verses
G
Je - sus Christ is born.
1. While shep - herds kept their
2. The shep - herds feared and
3. Down in a low - ly

Em
Am
D
G
watch - ing o'er si - lent flocks by night. Be -
trem - bled when lo, a - bove the earth rang
man - ger our hum - ble Christ was born, and

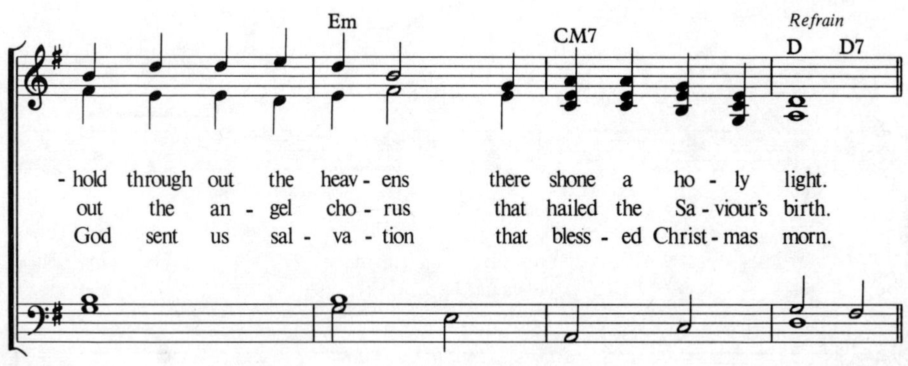
Em
CM7
Refrain
D D7
- hold through out the heav - ens there shone a ho - ly light.
out the an - gel cho - rus that hailed the Sa - viour's birth.
God sent us sal - va - tion that bless - ed Christ - mas morn.

4. When I was a seeker, I sought both night and day;
   I asked the Lord to help me, and he showed me the way.

5. He made me a watchman upon the city wall,
   And if I am a Christian, I am the least of all.

*Guitar chords and piano arrangement are not designed to be used together.

122. Let your light shine

Shirley Lewis Brown

Lyrical

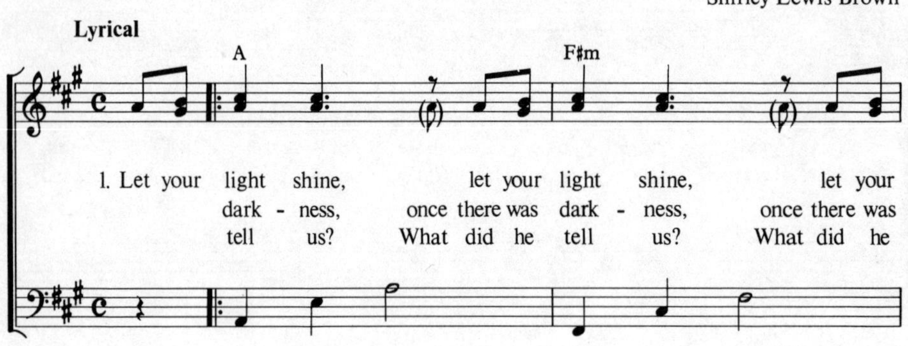
A
F♯m
1. Let your light shine, let your light shine, let your
dark - ness, once there was dark - ness, once there was
tell us? What did he tell us? What did he

DM7
A
light shine be - fore men, that they may
dark - ness up - on earth. Then God sent
tell us we should do? He said to

E
F♯m
see may see your good works, and
Je - sus, then God sent Je - sus to
love God, to love your neigh - bour, and

Bm
E
glo - - - ri - fy the
light the way, the
serve him. Let your

A
F♯m
Fa - ther, the Fa - ther, the
path - way, the path - way, the
light shine, let your light shine, let your

DM7
last time
A
A
Fa - ther who is in heav'n. 2. Once there was
path - way back to God. 3. What did he
light shine be - fore men.

123. Wondrous love

Traditional North American Melody
Arr. Betty Pulkingham

Peacefully

1. What won - drous love is this, O my soul, O my
2. When I was sink - ing down, sink - ing down, sink - ing
3. To God and to the Lamb I will sing, I will

soul? What won - drous love is this, O my soul? What
down, When I was sink - ing down, sink-ing down, When
sing. To God and to the Lamb I will sing. To

won-drous love is this that caused the Lord of bliss To
I was sink - ing down be - neath God's right-eous frown, Christ
God and to the Lamb who is the great I AM, While

bear the dread - ful curse for my soul, for my soul, To
laid a - side his crown for my soul, for my soul, Christ
thou-sands join the theme, I will sing, I will sing, While

1
2
bear the dread - ful curse for my soul.
laid a - side his crown for my soul.
thou - sands join the theme, I will sing.

4. And when from death I'm free, I'll sing on. I'll sing on,
And when from death I'm free, I'll sing on.
And when from death I'm free, I'll sing and joyful be,
And through eternity I'll sing on. I'll sing on,
And through eternity I'll sing on.

124. The King of glory

Rev. W. F. Jabusch

Traditional Israeli folk song
Arr. Betty Pulkingham

Well accented

Refrain
Em
C
The King of glo - ry comes, the na - tion re -

Em
C
joi - ces. O - pen the gates be - fore him,

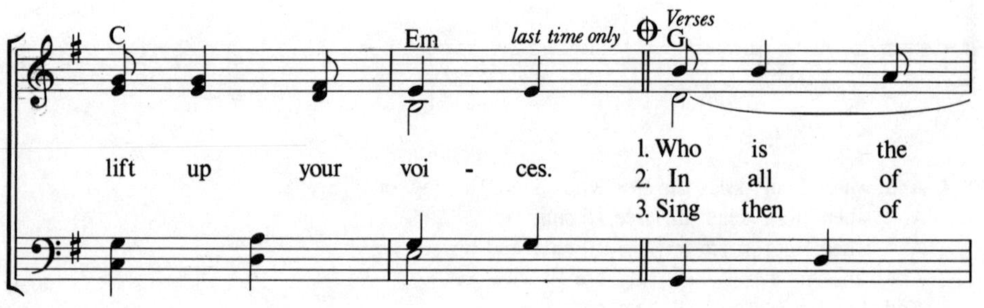
C
Em
last time only
Verses
G
lift up your voi - ces.
1. Who is the
2. In all of
3. Sing then of

D
G
C
King of glo - ry; how shall we call him?
Gal - i - lee, in ci - ty or vil - lage,
Da - vid's son, our Sav - ior and bro - ther;

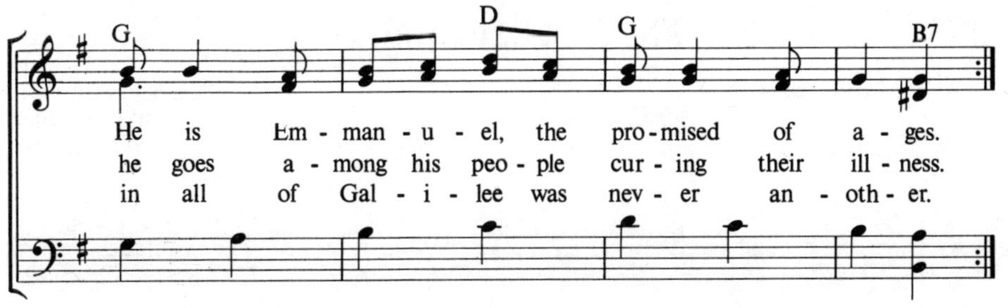
G
D
G
B7
He is Em - man - u - el, the pro-mised of a - ges.
he goes a - mong his peo - ple cur - ing their ill - ness.
in all of Gal - i - lee was nev - er an - oth - er.

Em
C
The King of glo - ry comes, the na -

Am
E
tion re - joi - - - - - ces.

4. He gave his life for us, the pledge of salvation.
He took upon himself the sins of the nation.

5. He conquered sin and death; he truly has risen,
And he will share with us his heavenly vision.

125. The foot washing song

Adapted from John 13

Shirley Lewis Brown
Arr. R. J. Batastini

Gracefully
Refrain
C
C
Put on the a - pron of hu - mil - i - ty;
F
C
G
C
serve your broth-er, wash his feet, that he may walk in the
C
F
G
C
Fine
way of the Lord, re - freshed, re - freshed.

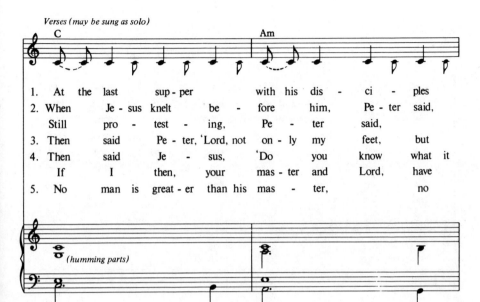

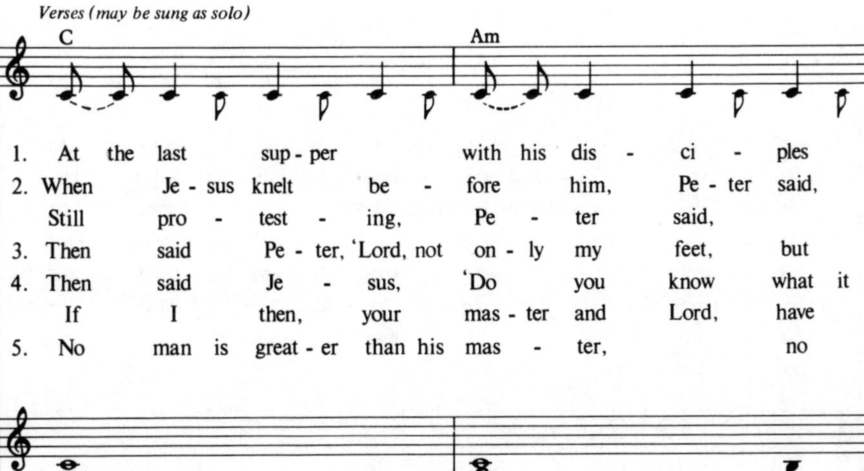
Verses (may be sung as solo)
C
Am
1. At the last sup - per with his dis - ci - ples
2. When Je - sus knelt be - fore him, Pe - ter said,
Still pro - test - ing, Pe - ter said,
3. Then said Pe - ter, 'Lord, not on - ly my feet, but
4. Then said Je - sus, 'Do you know what it
If I then, your mas - ter and Lord, have
5. No man is great - er than his mas - ter, no
(humming parts)

F
G
C
1. Je - sus rose from the ta - ble,
2. 'Lord, do you wash my feet?'
'Lord, you must nev - er wash my feet.'
3. al - so my hands and my head.'
4. is that I have done?
stooped to wash your feet,
5. mes - sen - ger than he who sent him.

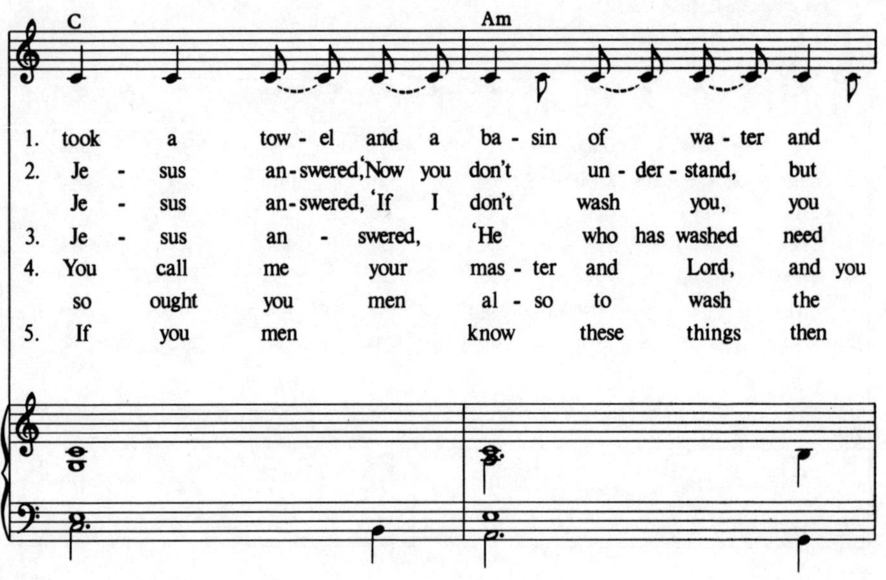
C
Am
1. took a tow - el and a ba - sin of wa - ter and
2. Je - sus an - swered,'Now you don't un - der - stand, but
Je - sus an - swered, 'If I don't wash you, you
3. Je - sus an - swered, 'He who has washed need
4. You call me your mas - ter and Lord, and you
so ought you men al - so to wash the
5. If you men know these things then

F
G
C
1. stooped to wash their feet. (Refrain)
2. la - ter on you will.' (Refrain)
have no part of me.'
3. on - ly wash his feet.' (Refrain)
4. speak the truth, for so I am. (Refrain)
feet of one an - oth - er.
5. hap - py are you if you do them.' (Refrain)

126. Were you there?

North American Spiritual

With deep reverence
1. Were you there when they cru - ci - fied my Lord? Were you
2. Were you there when they nailed him to the tree? Were you
3. Were you there when they laid him in the tomb? Were you
there when they cru - ci - fied my Lord?
there when they nailed him to the tree? Oh!
there when they laid him in the tomb?
some-times it caus - es me to tremble, tremble, tremble.
Were you there when they cru - ci - fied my Lord?
Were you there when they nailed him to the tree?
Were you there when they laid him in the tomb?

4. Were you there when he rose up from the dead? *(repeat)*
Oh!..,sometimes it causes me to shout 'Hallelujah!'
Were you there when he rose up from the dead?

128. Thine be the glory

Edmond Louis Budry
Tr. Richard Birch Hoyle

'Maccabaeus'
George Frederick Handel

With great dignity
1. Thine be the glo - ry, ri - sen, con-q'ring Son,
2. Lo, Je - sus meets us, ri - sen, from the tomb!
3. No more we doubt thee, glo - rious prince of life;
End - less is the vic - t'ry thou o'er death hast won;
Lov - ing - ly he greets us, scat - ters fear and gloom;
Life is nought with - out thee: aid us in our strife;
An - gels in bright rai - ment rolled the stone a - way,
Let the church with glad - ness hymns of tri - umph sing,
Make us more than con - q'rors, through thy death - less love;
Kept the fold - ed grave - clothes, where thy bo - dy lay.
For her Lord now liv - eth, death hath lost its sting.
Bring us safe through Jor - dan to thy home a - bove.

Refrain
Thine be the glo - ry, ris - en, con-q'ring Son,

End - less is the vic - t'ry thou o'er death hast won!

129. Hallelujah today!

Charles Wesley | Betty Pulkingham

Medium rock tempo

Am Em Am

1. Christ the Lord is ri - sen to - day:
2. Love's re - deem - ing work ___ is done;
3. Lives a - gain our glo - rious King!

F Em Am

Sons of men and an - gels say,
Fought the fight, the bat - tle won; Hal - le -
Where, O death, is now your sting?

G Am G Am G

lu - jah! Hal - le - lu - jah! Hal - le - - -

Am

- - - - lu - jah to - day!

G D

Raise your joys and tri - umphs high;
Death in vain for - bids him rise;
Once he died our souls to save;

G D

Sing, you hea - vens and you earth re - ply,
Christ has o - pened par - a - dise,
Where is your vic - to - ry, O grave?

Am G Am

Hal - - - le - - lu - - - - - -

final ending

Am Em A

- jah! Christ the Lord is ri - sen to - day!

4. Soar we now where Christ has led,
   Following our exalted Head. Hallelujah!
Made like him, like him we rise,
   Ours the cross, the grave, the skies. Hallelujah!

Bongo drums add a distinctive flavour to this contempory hymn setting.
Suggested rhythm for lines 3 and 4:

etc.

130. Christ the Lord is risen today

Charles Wesley

'Easter Hymn'
from Lyra Davidica
Descant. Betty Pulkingham

Triumphantly

Optional descant (voice or trumpet)
Hal - le - lu, Ha - le - lu - jah!
1. Christ the Lord is risen to - day:
2. Love's re - deem - ing work is done;
3. Lives a - gain our glo - rious King!

Hal - - - - le - lu - jah! Hal - le -
Hal - - - - - - le - lu - jah!
Sons of men and
Fought the fight, the
Where, O death, is

- lu, Hal - le - lu - jah! Hal - - - - le - lu - jah!
an gels say, -
bat - tle won, - Hal - - - - le - lu - jah!
now thy sting? -

Hal - le - lu, Hal - le - lu - jah!
Raise your joys and tri - umphs high;
Death in vain for bids him rise,
Once he died our souls to save,

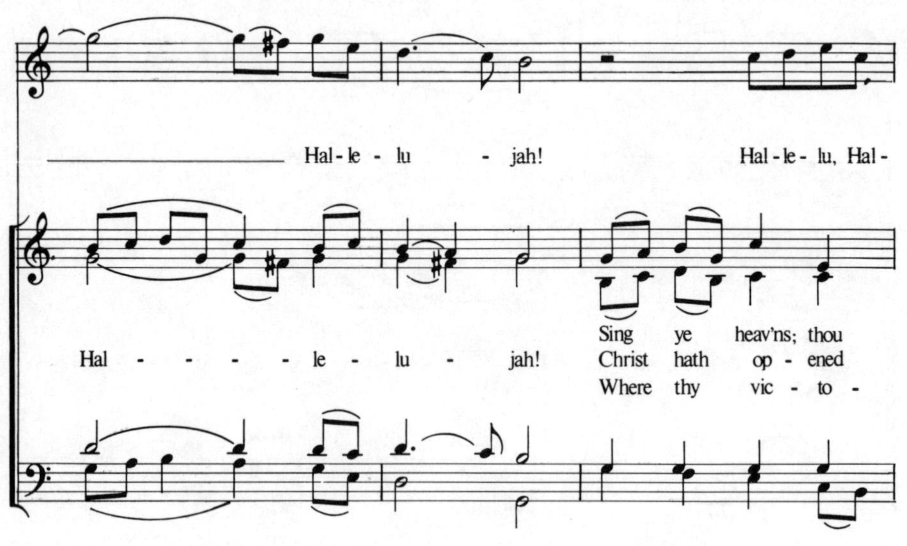
Hal - le - lu - jah! Hal - le - lu, Hal -
Hal - - - - - le - lu - jah!
Sing ye heav'ns; thou
Christ hath op - ened
Where thy vic - to -

- le - lu - jah! Hal - le - lu - jah!
earth re - ply,
par - ra - dise,
-ry, O grave?
Hal - - - - - le - lu - - jah!

4. Soar we now where Christ has led,
   Following our exalted Head:
   Made like him, like him we rise;
   Ours the cross, the grave, the skies;
   Hallelujah!

131. He will fill your hearts today

Refrain: Mrs. C. H. Morris
Verses: Betty Pulkingham

Arr. Betty Pulkingham

Skipping along
Refrain
C
F
C
He will fill your hearts to-day to o - ver-flow - ing, as the
G7
C
Lord comman - ded you, 'bring your ves - sels, not a few,' he will
F
C
fill your hearts to-day to o - ver-flow - ing with his
G
C
Fine
Ho - ly Ghost and power.

Martial
Verses
F
C
1. When the day of Pen - te - cost had come, the be -
2. Suddenly a noise from the sky, which
3. Then they looked up and saw, they
4. All of them were filled with the Ho - ly Ghost, with the
F
C
liev - ers were gath - er'd to - geth - er, were
soun - ded like a strong wind ___ blow - ing, a
saw what looked like ___ tongues of fire,
Ho - ly Ghost and power. They be -

F
C
gath - er'd to - geth - er in one place, of one
strong wind blow - ing by, filled the whole
tongues of fire spread-ing out, to each
- gan to speak in oth - er lan - gua - ges, in oth - er
Am
G
Refrain
mind as the Lord had com - mand - ed.
house, the noise kept on grow - ing.
one, spread - ing out to touch the peo - ple.
languages he gave them in that hour!

132. Come, Holy Ghost

Louis Lambillotte

With dignity and breadth
1. Come, Ho - ly Ghost cre - a - tor blest, Vouchsafe with - in our souls to rest; Come with thy grace and heav'nly aid, And fill the hearts which thou hast made, And fill the hearts which thou hast made.
2. To thee the com - fort - er we cry; To thee the gift of God most high; The fount of life, the fire of love, The soul's a - noint - ing from a - bove, The soul's a - noint - ing from a - bove.
3. The sev'n-fold gifts of grace are thine, O fin - ger of the hand de - vine. True pro - mise of the Fa - ther thou, Who dost the tongue with speech en - dow, Who dost the tongue with speech en - dow.

4. Thy light to every sense impart,
   And shed thy love in every heart;
Thine own unfailing might supply,
   To strengthen our infirmity.

5. Drive far away our ghostly foe,
   And thine abiding peace bestow;
If thou be our preventing guide,
   No evil can our steps betide.

133. Planted wheat

Jeff Cothran

'Hashual'
Traditional Hebrew Melody
Arr. Jeff Cothran

Introduction
Simply and lightly *
Recorder and voices; Noo Noo Noo *(etc)*

Verse

MEN: 1. Plan - ted wheat, with - in the wheat-fields, wait - ing till the summer
MEN: 2. Je - sus rose, we can - not see him; he is seat - ed at the
ALL: 3. Je - sus Christ is Lord of the har - vest. Soon in glo - ry he will

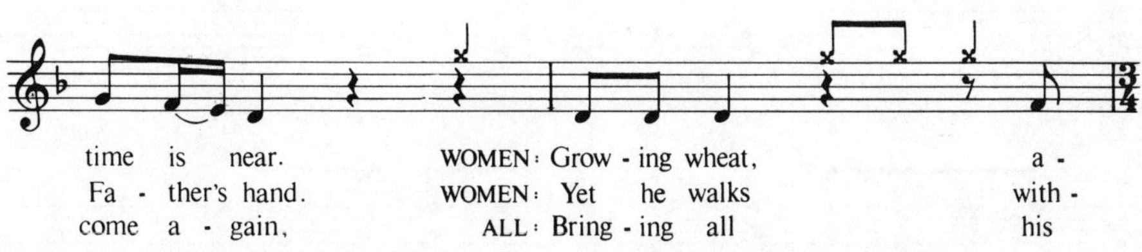
time is near. WOMEN: Grow - ing wheat, a -
Fa - ther's hand. WOMEN: Yet he walks with -
come a - gain, ALL: Bring - ing all his

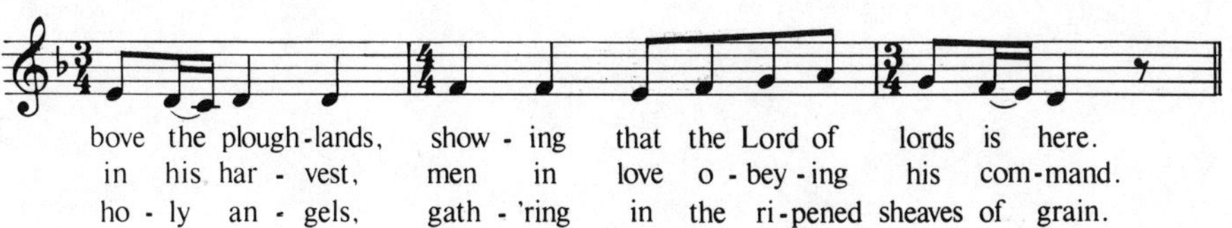
bove the plough-lands, show - ing that the Lord of lords is here.
in his har - vest, men in love o - bey - ing his com-mand.
ho - ly an - gels, gath - 'ring in the ri-pened sheaves of grain.

* Wood block or finger cymbals

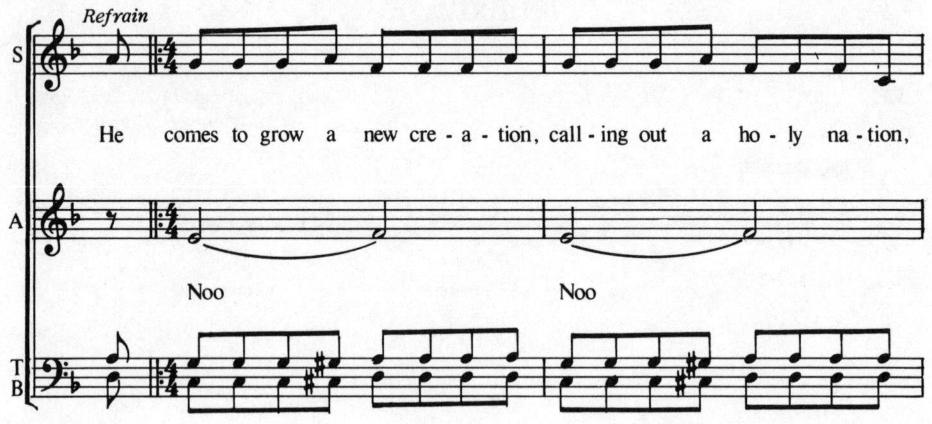
Refrain
S
A
T
B
He comes to grow a new cre - a - tion, call - ing out a ho - ly na - tion,
Noo
Noo
He comes to grow a new cre - a - tion, call - ing out a ho - ly na - tion,

Fine
S
A
T
B
all who will be - lieve, and all who will re - ceive. He
Noo Noo Noo Noo Noo Noo
all who will be - lieve, and all who will re - ceive. He

Fresh Sounds

Contents

hallelujah!

songs of praise and thanksgiving

1. 'Sanna

Traditional
Arr. Betty Pulkingham

With fervency of expression

1.
San - na,* san - na - ni - na, san - na, san - na, san - na,
2.
san - na, san - na, san - na, san - na - ni - na,
1.
2.
san - na, san - na, san - na.
San-

*This is a shortened form of the word 'hosanna.'

This song may be sung most effectively by voices in four-part harmony, unaccompanied.

2. Hail to the Lord's anointed

Based on Psalm 72
James Montgomery

'Yeldall'
Betty Pulkingham

Bright and well-accented
D
Am7
D
Am7
D
A
D
1. Hail to the Lord's a - noint - ed, Great Da - vid's
Hail in the time ap - point - ed, His reign on
2. He shall come down like show - ers Up - on the
And love, joy, hope, like flow - ers, Spring in his
C
A7
D
great-er Son!
earth be - gun! He comes to break op-
fruit-ful earth,
path to birth: Be-fore him on the
Am7
F
A7
pres - sion, To set the cap - tive free;
moun-tains Shall peace, the her - ald go;
8

D
Em
A
D
D Maj7
Am7
To take a - way trans - gres - sion, And rule
And right - eous - ness in foun - tains From hill
D
Am7
D.S.
D
final ending
in e - qui - ty.
to val - ley flow.

3. Kings shall bow down before him,
   And gold and incense bring;
   All nations shall adore him,
   His praise all people sing;
   For he shall have dominion
   O'er every sea and shore;
   His kingdom still increasing,
   A kingdom for evermore.

4. O'er every foe victorious,
   He on his throne shall rest;
   From age to age more glorious,
   All blessing and all-blest:
   The tide of time shall never
   His covenant remove;
   His name shall stand for ever,
   His changeless name of love.

3. Crown him with many crowns

Matthew Bridges
Godfrey Thring

'Diademata'
George Job Elvey
Descant by Betty Pulkingham

With vigour
Descant
3. Crown him with ma - ny crowns, Who tri - umphed o'er the grave, And rose vic - to - rious for those he came to save, His glo - ries, his
5. Crown him the Lord of heav'n, En-throned in worlds a - bove, Crown him the King to whom is giv'n the name of love, Crown him, crown
1. Crown him with ma - ny crowns, The lamb up - on his throne; Hark! how the heav'n - ly an - them drowns All mu - sic but its own; A - wake, my soul, and
2. Crown him the Son of God Be - fore the worlds be-gan, And ye, who tread where he hath trod, Crown him the Son of man; Who ev' - ry grief hath
3. Crown him the Lord of life, Who tri-umphed o'er the grave, And rose vic - to - rious in the strife For those he came to save; His glo - ries now we

glo - ries now — we sing, Who died e - ter - nal
him with ma - ny crowns, As thrones be - fore — him
sing Of him who died for thee, And
known That wrings the hu - man breast, And
sing Who died, and rose on high, Who
life to bring and lives that death may die.
fall, crown him, for he is Lord - of all.
hail him as thy match - less King Through all e - ter - ni - ty.
takes and bears them for his own, That all in him may rest.
died, e - ter - nal life to bring, And lives that death may die.

4. Crown him of lords the Lord,
 Who over all doth reign,
Who once on earth, the incarnate Word,
 For ransomed sinners slain,
Now lives in realms of light,
 Where saints with angels sing
Their songs before him day and night,
 Their God, Redeemer, King.

5. Crown him the Lord of heav'n,
 Enthroned in worlds above;
Crown him the King, to whom is giv'n
 The wondrous name of Love.
Crown him with many crowns,
 As thrones before him fall,
Crown him, ye kings, with many crowns,
 For he is King of all.

4. The God of Abraham praise

Jewish Doxology
Para. Thomas Olivers

'Leoni'
Arr. Meyer Lyon
Descant by Betty Pulkingham

With vigour
(Descant) 5. The whole tri - umph-ant host give thanks to
God on high, 'Hail Fa - - - - ther, Son and
Ho - ly Ghost,' they cry. Hail A - bra-ham's God and
1. The God of A- braham praise, Who reigns en - throned a-
2. He by him - self hath sworn: I on his oath de-
3. There dwells the Lord, our King, The Lord, our right - eous-
bove; An - cient of ev - er - last - ing days, And
pend; I shall, on ea - gle wings up - borne, To
ness, Tri - umph - ant o'er the world and sin, The
God of love; To him up - lift your
heav'n as - cend: I shall be - hold his
Prince of peace; On Si - on's sa - cred

mine, we join ___ the heav'n-ly lays, All might and
voice, At whose supreme com - mand, From earth we rise, and
face, I shall his power a - dore, And sing the won-ders
height His king - dom he main - tains, And, glo - rious with his
ma - jes - ty, and ___ end- less praise. A - - - - - - - - - - -men.
seek the joys At his right hand.
of his grace For - ev - - - - er - more. A - - - - - - - - - men.
saints in light, For - ev - - - - er reigns.

4. The God who reigns on high
 The great archangels sing,
And 'Holy, holy, holy', cry,
 Almighty King!
Who was, and is, the same,
 And evermore shall be:
Eternal Father, great I AM,
 We worship thee.

5. The whole triumphant host
 Give thanks to God on high;
'Hail, Father, Son and Holy Ghost!'
 They ever cry;
Hail, Abraham's God and mine!
 I join the heav'nly lays;
All might and majesty are thine,
 And endless praise.

5. Hallelujah! Gonna sing all about it

Roy Turner
Arr. Betty Pulkingham

With a bounce
E
E7
Hal - le - lu - jah! Gon - na sing all a-bout it. Hal - le-
A
E
lu - jah! Gon - na shout all a-bout it. Hal - le - lu - jah! Can't
B7
E
live with-out it, praise God. (Praise God) Now I'm liv - ing in a
Ped.
E7
A
new cre - a - tion, now I'm drink-ing at the well of sal - va - tion.
E
A
E, A
E
Now there is no con - dem-na - tion, praise God. (Praise God.)

6. # Hallelujah, my Father

Tim Cullen

With quiet devotion

Hal-le - lu - jah, my Fa - - ther, for giv-ing us your
Son; send-ing him in - to the world to be giv-en up for
men, know - ing we would bruise him and smite him from the
earth. Hal-le - lu - jah, my Fa - - ther, in his
death is my birth. Hal-le - lu - jah, my

Fa - - ther, in his life is my life.

7. Praise my God with the tambourine

Adapted from Judith 16: 1, 13-19
Jerusalem Bible

Diane Davis

Boldly, with vigour

Refrain

Am Em Am

Praise my God with the tam - bou - rine; Sing to the Lord with the

Em Am Am *Fine*

1. 2.

cym - - - - - - - bals. - bals.

Verses

D Am

1. I will sing a new song to my God. 'You are
2. 'May your whole cre - a - tion serve you. When you
3.'Should the moun - tains top - ple to min - gle with the waves, should

D
Am
D
1,2.
great, you are glo-ri-ous, won - der-ful - ly
speak, things come in-to being; no-one can re-sist your
rocks melt like wax be - - - - fore your face, to

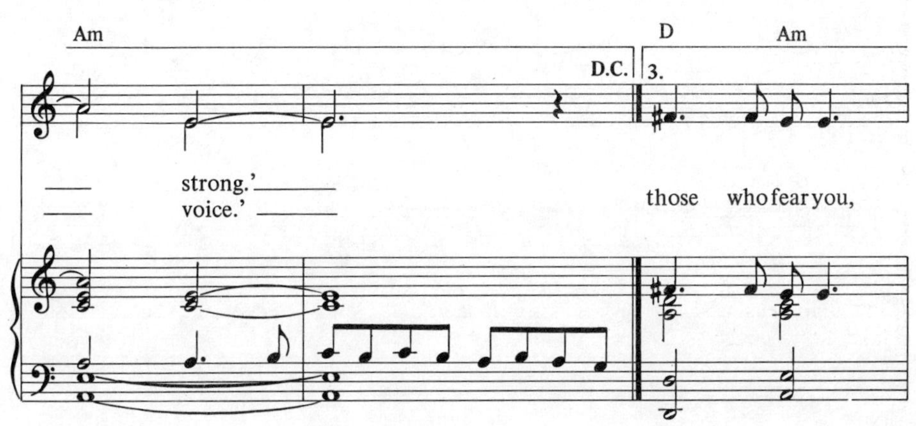
Am
D.C.
D
Am
3.
strong.'
voice.'
those who fear you,

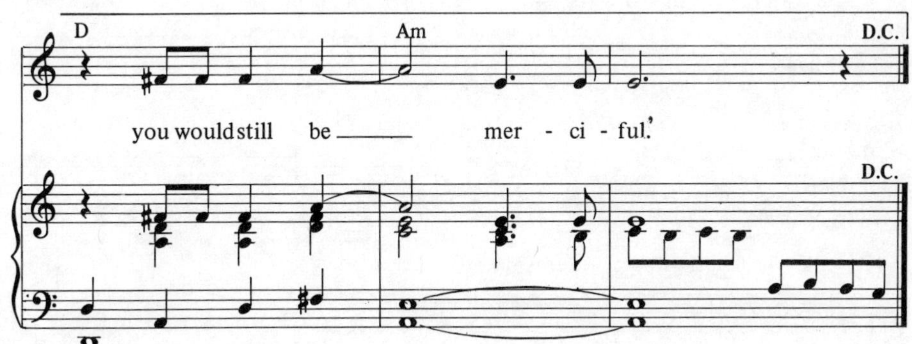
D
Am
D.C.
you would still be mer - ci - ful.'
D.C.

8. The dancing heart

Roy Turner
Arr. Betty Pulkingham
With joyful abandon
D A7 D G A7 D Refrain A7 D A
1. Da - vid danced be - fore the Lord, he danced with all his might; his
heart was filled with ho - ly joy, his spi - rit was so light.
Mi - chal through the win - dow looked, to cri - ti - cise did start, she
did - n't know that Da - vid had got a danc - ing heart. Oh, the
Ho - ly Ghost will set your feet a - danc - ing! The

(Hal - le - lu - jah)
A
D
Ho - ly Ghost will fill you through and through. The
G
Ho - ly Ghost will set your feet a - danc - ing, and
A
A7
D
set your heart a - danc - ing too!

2. David danced before the Lord to magnify his name;
In God's almighty presence he felt no sense of shame;
The oil of gladness flowed that day, it quickened every part;
He hadn't only dancing feet, he had a dancing heart.

3. Out of Egypt long ago the Israelites were led;
By a mighty miracle they all were kept and fed;
Through the Red sea they were brought, the waters stood apart,
And God gave sister Miriam a dance down in her heart.

4. There was a celebration - upon the Red sea shore;
Timbrels rang, desert sands became a dancing floor;
The people sang and praised God there, he made the gloom depart,
And put a dance of love and joy a-deep down in their hearts.

5. The prodigal was far away - wandering out in sin,
But he came back to father's house and father took him in;
He put a robe upon his son - the merriment did start,
The prodigal got dancing shoes to match his dancing heart.

6. The father's house with music rang to welcome home the son;
Wine was flowing full and free, all misery was gone;
The elder brother looking on complained it wasn't fair;
He hadn't got a dancing heart like all the others there.

7. Now many saints are cold and bound by unbelief today,
They want the blessings of the Lord but worry what men say;
Oh, let the Lord have full control, from dead traditions part,
And he will set you free within, you'll have a dancing heart.

9. Now let us sing

Traditional
Arr. Betty Pulkingham

With a swing
A
Sing 'til the pow'r of the Lord comes down.
Now let us sing.
Now let us sing.
E
Sing 'til the pow'r of the Lord comes down.
Lift up your hands,
A
D
Lift up your hands, don't be a - fraid. Now let us
don't be a - fraid.
A
E
Fine
A
sing 'til the pow'r of the Lord comes down.
sing 'til the pow'r of the Lord comes down. Now let us sing.

Possible variations:

Now let us (praise, pray, love.......) *or*
Lift up your (hearts, heads.......)

10. Sing praise to the Lord forever

'Jacob's Song'

Capo 4 (C)

Jacob Krieger
Adapted by Mikel Kennedy

With strength, briskly

Refrain
E(C)
A(F)
B(G)
(Part1) Sing praise to the Lord for - ev - er and ev -
(Part 2) Sing

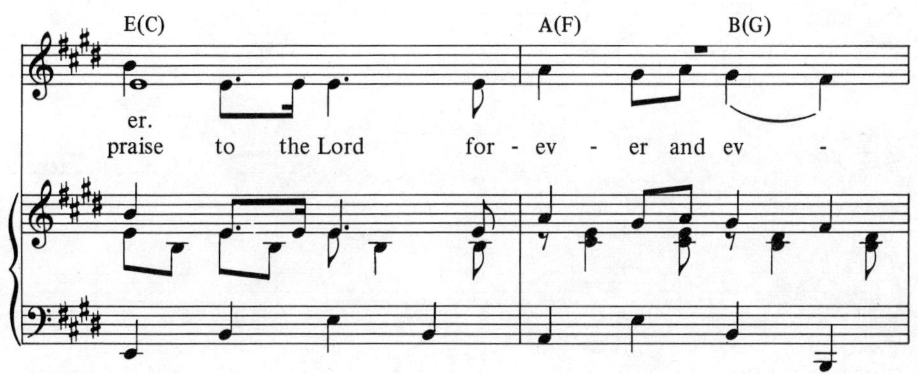

E(C)
A(F)
B(G)
er.
praise to the Lord for - ev - er and ev -

E(C)
A(F)
B(G)
Call un - to him for hope in sal - va -
er.

E(C)
A(F)
B(G)
tion.
Call un - to him for hope in sal - va -
E(C)
A(F)
E(C)
B(G)
E(C)
tion. Sing praise, al - le - lu - ia, sing praise, al - le - lu! Sing
A(F)
E(C)
last time
B(G)
E(C)
praise, al - le - lu - ia, sing praise, al - le - lu!
C♯m(Am)
B(G)
C♯m(Am)
1. Oh, sing praise to our Fa - ther in
2. Oh, sing praise to the Son of
3. Oh, sing praise to the Spi - rit of

B(G)
C♯m(Am)
F♯(D)
heav'n. Sing un - to the
God. Call un - to his
God. Sing to the Lord of
B(G)
B7(G7)
D.S.
A(F)
E(C)
Lord.
name.
life.
Sing praise, al- le - lu! Sing
praise, al- le - lu! Sing
Broaden
A(F)
E(C)
B(G)
E(C)
praise, al - le - lu - ia, sing praise, al - le - lu!

11. Sing, sing alleluia

Capo 2 (Am)

Nancy Carr Newman

Joyously
Bm(Am)
A(G)
Bm(Am)
Refrain
Bm(Am)
A(G)
Bm(Am)
Sing, sing al - le - lu - ia, sing
Emsus2 (Dmsus2)
Em(Dm)
F#7(E7)
glo - - - - - ry Je - sus Christ.
Bm(Am)
A(G)
Bm(Am)
Sing, sing al - le - lu - ia, be-
Em7(Dm7)
Bm(Am)
last time
hold the Lamb of God.

Em(Dm)
Bm(Am)
Em(Dm)
3
Bm(Am)
1. He rules the heavens, master of the earth.
3. place your trust in him.
2. Who is the King of glory? What is his name?
3. Come ye who seek the Lord,
G(F)
D(C)
F#7(E7)
D.S.
1. All men now join together to praise the Lord.
3. Jesus will set you free to follow him.
D.S.
2. Jesus of Nazareth is his name.
D.S.
Bm(Am)
A(G)
Bm(Am)
A(G)
Bm(Am)
(Part 1) Sing, sing al-le-lu-ia.
2nd time
All
(lu-ia.) (Part 2) Sing, sing al-le-lu-ia.
Optional descant for refrain
Sing, sing, sing al-le-lu-ia, sing glo-ry Je-sus Christ.
Sing, sing, sing al-le-lu-ia, be-hold the Lamb of God.

12. Sing to the Lord

Donald Fishel
Arr. Betty Pulkingham
Strongly accented
C
f
Sing to the Lord a new song,
Am
sing to the Lord a new song,
F
sing to the Lord, sing
Dm
to the Lord a new song.
G
last time
C
Am
1. God made the world in sev - en days.
2. God said to Mo - ses, 'Go and set my peo - ple free.
3. Je - sus said to Pe - ter, 'Come on, I'm call - ing you. I
4. Come on my bro - ther, won't you turn to Je - sus now, he

C
Am
A - dam sinn'd and then all men fell a - way.
I will be your guide, just al - ways fol - low me.'
know the way is hard, but I'll al - ways see you through.'
knows that you're a sin - ner but he loves you an - y - how.
C
Am
Je - sus came to re - deem my soul. He
Mo - ses led the peo - ple through the part - ed Red Sea, then they
Pe - ter said, 'My Lord, I'm a sin - ful man.' Then he
Je - sus paid the price for your sal - va - tion, just
F
G
died up - on the cross and he made me whole!
sang, and they danced, and they had a jub - i - lee!
threw down his net, and to the Lord he ran!
call up - on his name and you're a new cre - a - - - tion!
cresc.
last time
F
Dm
C
sing to the Lord a new song.

13. We will sing to the Lord our God

Richard Gullen

With rhythmic drive
Refrain
G C G F C G
f We will sing to the Lord our God,
F C G
mighty and splendid is he! We will
C G F C G
sing to our Saviour and King,
last time
F C G
1. 2.
glorious in majesty. We will

F
mp
A
G
1. Here is the Lord, he is a - mong us;
mp
2. Here is the Lord, let us walk with him;
mp
F
A
G
let us wor - ship him to - geth - er.
he will lead and guide us through his land.
F
Am
Here is the Lord, he is a-mong
Here is the Lord, let us

G
F
us;
let us
walk with him;
we will

C
G
cresc.
D.S.
praise him all to-geth - er.
We will
D.S.
walk in peace through-out his land.
We will
D.S.
cresc.

F
C
G
Glo-ri-ous in ma - jes-ty.

14. This is the day of the Lord

Charles High

Liltingly
S
A
T
B
This is the day— of the Lord. This is the day— of the
Lord. —
This is the day— of the
Lord. — Al - le - lu, —
al - le - lu.

A good song for unaccompanied singing, using only 'fingertip' clapping (the fingertips of the right hand against the palm of the left.)

Adapt verses to suit occasion, such as:

1. This is the (feast.....birthday.....service.....song) of the Lord.
2. We are the people of the Lord.
3. These are the praises of the Lord.

kneel and adore him

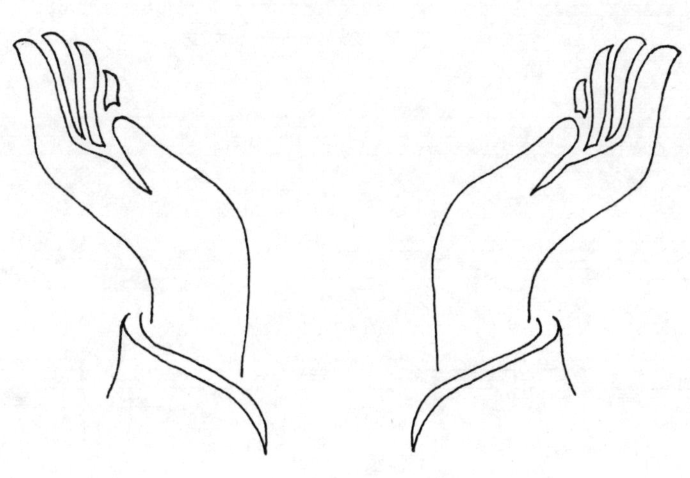

songs of worship

SECTION 2

KNEEL AND ADORE

SONGS OF WORSHIP

15. Turn me, O God

Quietly and slowly Jodi Page

Refrain
D
Turn me, O God, and
A7
D
I shall be turned.
1.
2.
Fine
G
A
D
1. Though I wan-der through des - - - o - la-tion,
OMIT
2. Cre - ate in me a new heart.
3. You have led us out of bon - dage,
verse 1 only

G A D
I will find you there.
I would see your face.
you have kept us well.
G A D
Though the wa-ters o'er - whelm my soul,
Take not your ho - ly Spi - rit from me,
Ev-en in the face of our com-plaint,
A7 D D.C.
ev - en so you are Lord.
D.C.
OMIT
I would see your face.
you have loved us still.
verse 1 only
D.C.

16. Jesus, I love you

Kathleen Thomerson

Simply and softly, not too slow
love, love you.
Je - sus, I love you, Je - sus, I love you,
Je - sus, I love you, take my life.
1. Life is your
2. Now I have
3. Love reach-es
gift, I give my heart, kneel and a - dore you, and — I
seen the love of God. He has poured out the Spi-rit of
out both near and far, and so we fol-low where— you
1-2.
3.
know that Je - sus, I fol-low, Je - sus, I
truth.— lead us. Je - sus, I love you, Je - sus, I

fol-low, Je - sus, I fol-low, all my life.
love you. Je - sus, I love you, take my life.

17. Jesus, Jesus

May be sung as a 2, 3, or 4-part round.

Anon.
Arr. Betty Pulkingham

Slowly, fervently

1 Em D Em Bm7 2 Em D

Je - sus, Je - sus, let me tell you

Em Bm7 3 Em D Em Bm7

what I — know. You have giv - en us your — spi - rit;

4 Em D Em Bm7 *final ending* E

we love you so. so.

18. The Shepherd of my soul

Kathleen Thomerson

Tenderly
1. I___ sing to the shep-herd of my soul all the day as he
2. I___ sing to the shep-herd of my soul all the night for the
3. All my life, O shep-herd of my soul, I will sing with a
leads me through this_ world. To fol-low him,__ to tru-ly fol-low
path is clear to___ him. And when I sleep,_ he makes a shel-ter
heart that's full of___ joy. To fol-low you___ is just to trust that
in his way is to live a life of love.
of his light; when I wake he leads me on.
you will bring all your sheep in - to the fold.
Refrain
All I am I of-fer Je - sus, sing - ing praises un-to him.

Oh, my soul, give thanks to Je - sus, for he is your shep-herd-king.

19. Come into his presence

Anon.

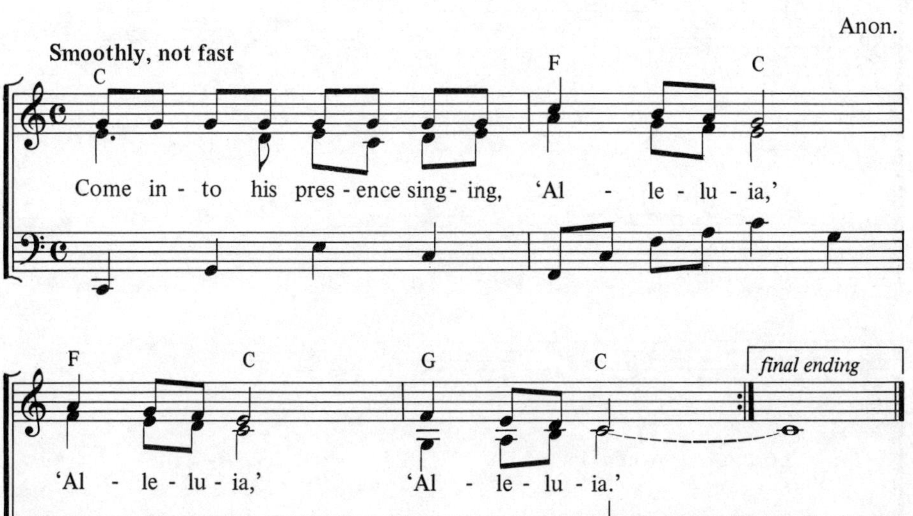
Smoothly, not fast
C
F
C
Come in - to his pres - ence sing - ing, 'Al - le - lu - ia,'
F
C
G
C
final ending
'Al - le - lu - ia,' 'Al - le - lu - ia.'

Other verses may be added:

Come into his presence singing,
'Jesus is Lord'..........
'Worthy the Lamb'.......
'Glory to God'.......

20. My song is love unknown

Samuel Crossman
John Ireland
Fervently, not slow
1. My song is love un - known, My Sa-viour's love to me; Love to the love-less shown, That they might love - - - - - ly be. O who am I, that for my sake My Lord should take frail flesh and die?
2. He came from his blest throne Sal - va - tion to be-stow; But men made strange, and none The longed-for Christ would know: But O, my friend, my friend in-deed, Who at my need his life did spend.
3. Some-times they strew his way And his sweet prais-es sing; Re - sound - ing all the day Ho - san - nas to their King. Then 'Cru - ci - fy!' is all their breath, And for his death they thirst and cry.

4. They rise and needs will have
My dear Lord made away;
A murderer they save,
The Prince of life they slay,
  Yet cheerful he to suff'ring goes,
  That he his foes from thence might free.

5. In life, no house, no home
My Lord on earth might have;
In death, no friendly tomb,
But what a stranger gave.
  What may I say? Heaven was his home;
  But mine the tomb wherein he lay.

6. Here might I stay and sing,
No story so divine;
Never was love, dear King,
Never was grief like thine.
  This is my friend, in whose sweet praise
  I all my days could gladly spend.

21. I love the name of Jesus

Capo 3 (D)

Kathleen Thomerson

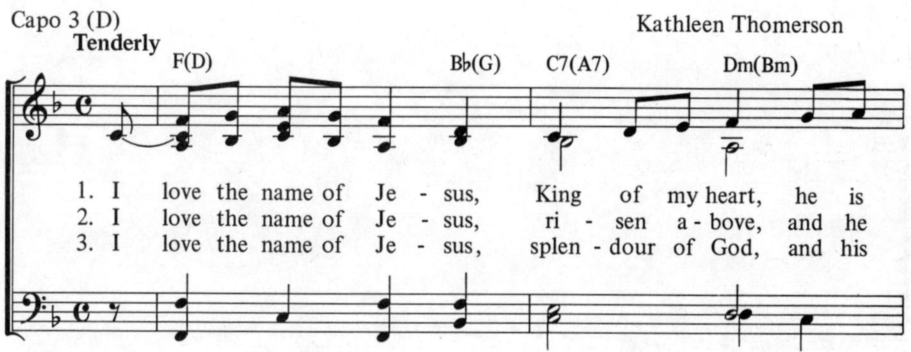
Tenderly
F(D)
Bb(G)
C7(A7)
Dm(Bm)
1. I love the name of Je - sus, King of my heart, he is
2. I love the name of Je - sus, ri - sen a - bove, and he
3. I love the name of Je - sus, splen - dour of God, and his

Gm(Em)
C7(A7)
F(D)
Bb(G)
ev' - ry - thing to me. I bless the name of Je - sus,
loves and prays for me. I bless the name of Je - sus,
face I long to see. I bless the name of Je - sus,

C7(A7) Dm(Bm) Gm(Em) C7(A7) F(D) F7(D7)
reign in my life, show the Fa-ther's love so free.
rul-ing on high with a glo-rious ma-jes-ty.
shep-herd of men; by his side I now can be.
B♭(G) F(D)
Spi-rit of love, spi-rit of power,
Gm(Em) G7(E7) C(A) C7(A7) F(D) B♭(G)
I love the name of Je-sus,
shine through e-ter-ni-ty. I praise the name of Je-sus,
I praise the name of Je-sus,
C7(A7) Dm(Bm) Gm(Em) C7(A7) F(D)
light of the world, let me walk each day with thee.
Lord of my life, for he died to set me free.
for he is love, and that love he gives to me.

22. Blessed be the name

Capo 1 (E)

Anon.
Arr. Betty Pulkingham

Gently
F(E)
F7(E7)
Bb(A)
F(E)
1. Bless - ed be the name, bless - ed be the name,
C7(B7)
Bless - ed be the name of the Lord.
F(E)
F7(E7)
Bb(A)
F(E)
Bless - ed be the name, bless - ed be the name,
Bb(A)
F/C(E/B)
C7(B7)
F(E)
Bb(A)
F(E)
Bless - ed be the name of the Lord.

2. Jesus is the name, Jesus is the name,
Jesus is the name of the Lord. } *repeat*

3. Worthy to be praised, worthy to be praised,
Worthy to be praised is the Lord. } *repeat*

23. Glory

Capo 3 (D)

Mimi Farra

Freely
F(D)
F Maj7 (D Maj7)
F +6 (D +6)
C7 (A7)
1. Sing to the Lord, sing to the Lord of Lords.
Flowing
Gm7 (Em7)
C7 (A7)
Glo - - - - - - - ry, glo - - - - - - - ry,
Gm7 (Em7)
C7 (A7)
glo - - - - - - - ry, glo - - - - - - ry,
F(D) C7 (A7) F(D) F(D) C7 (A7) F(D)
1.
2.
Fine
1.
2. glo - ry to the Lord. Son. Lamb.
3.
4. glo - ry Je - sus Christ.
glo - ry to the Lord. Son. Lamb.
glo - ry Je - sus Christ.

F(D) F Maj7 (D Maj7)

2, 3. Sing, — oh sing to the Son / Lamb of — God,

4. Sing, oh sing to the Word of God, the

F +6(D +6) C7(A7) D.S.

Sing, for he is — wor - - - thy of —

D.S.*

Word made flesh in — Je - sus — Christ.

D.S.

* Following verse 4 the refrain may be repeated several times, beginning softly, increasing volume and momentum as repetitions occur, and adding the following descant on the final refrain:

Descant (for soprano solo or a few treble voices)

Glo - - - - ry, glo - - - - - ry, glo - - - - - - -
- - - - - - - ry, glo - ry Je - sus Christ. Glo - - - - - - - - -
- - - - ry, glo - ry, glo - - - - - - - - ry, glo - ry Je - sus Christ.

24. Sweet Jesus

Anon.
Arr. Life and Soul Group

Easy rock beat
E A E G# C#m
Sweet Je - - - - - - - -
A E G# C#m A
sus, sweet Je - - - - - - - - - - sus,
E E7
li - ly of the val-ley, bright as the morning

A
G♯m
F♯m
star. Sweet Je - - - - - - - - - sus, sweet
E
G♯
C♯m
A
E
Je - - - - - - - - - sus, he's the God of ev' - ry
B7
A
E
na-tion, bless his name.

2. How I love him, how I love him,
   Lily of the valley, bright as the morning star.
   How I love him, how I love him,
   He's the God of every nation,
      Bless his name.

3. Jesus loves you.....
4. Sweet Jesus.....

25. Sweet Jesus

Paul Goodwin
Arr. Betty Pulkingham

Simply

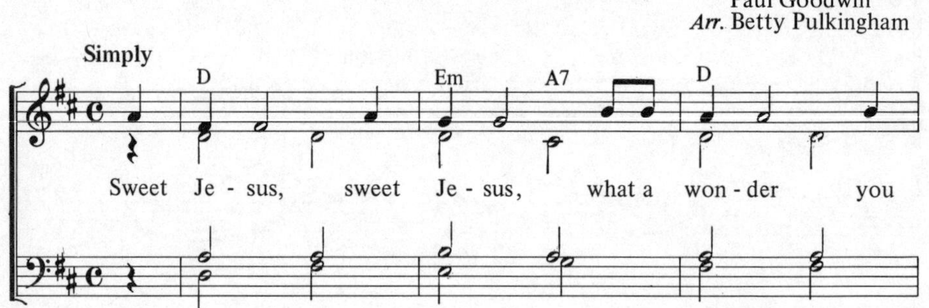
D
Em
A7
D
Sweet Je - sus, sweet Je - sus, what a won - der you

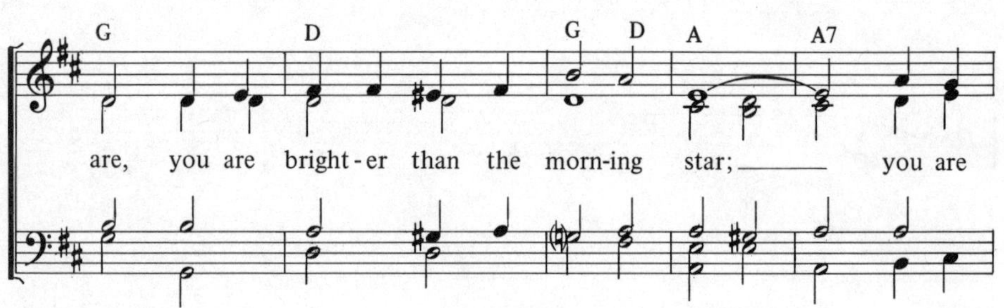
G
D
G
D
A
A7
are, you are bright - er than the morn-ing star; you are

D
Em
A7
D
D7
fair - er, much fair - er than the li - ly that grows by the

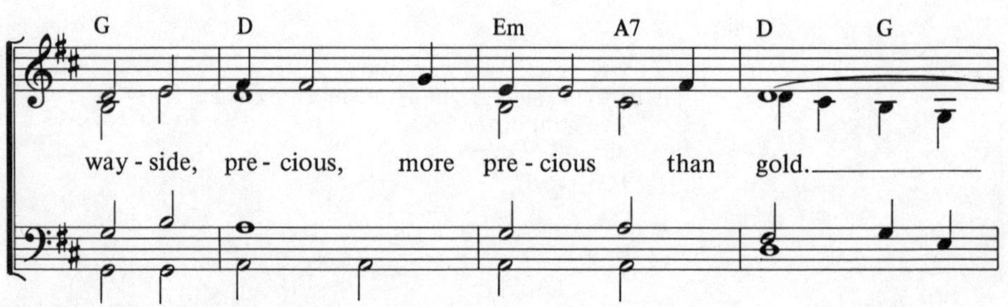
G
D
Em
A7
D
G
way - side, pre - cious, more pre - cious than gold.

D D7 G D
You are the rose of Sha-ron, the fair-est of the

A7 D G D A
fair, you are all my heart could e'er de - sire.

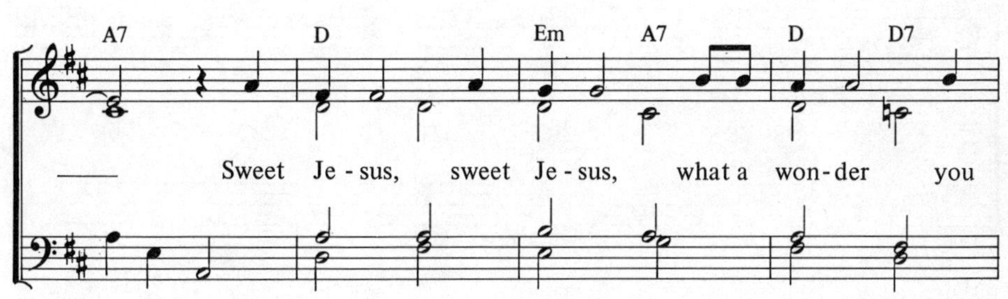
A7 D Em A7 D D7
Sweet Je-sus, sweet Je-sus, what a won-der you

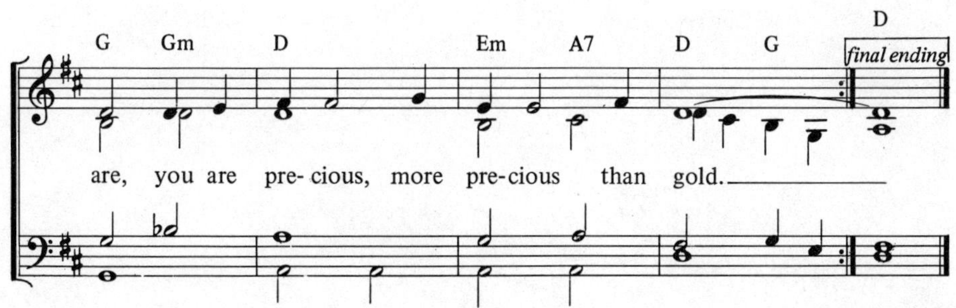
G Gm D Em A7 D G D
final ending
are, you are pre-cious, more pre-cious than gold.

26. God gives peace like a river

Anon.
Arr. Betty Pulkingham

Steadily
E
E7
A
God gives peace like a riv - er, peace like a
B7(E*)
E
F♯
B7
riv - er, God gives peace like a riv - er in my soul.
E
E7
A
God gives peace like a riv - er, peace like a
B7(E*)
C♯m(E*)
F♯m(E/B*) B7
E
A
E
riv - er, God gives peace like a riv - er in my soul.

Other verses may be added:
God gives love ..... joy ..... faith ..... hope ..... praise ... *etc.*

*Use these chords if guitar plays alone.

27. O worship the Lord in the beauty of holiness

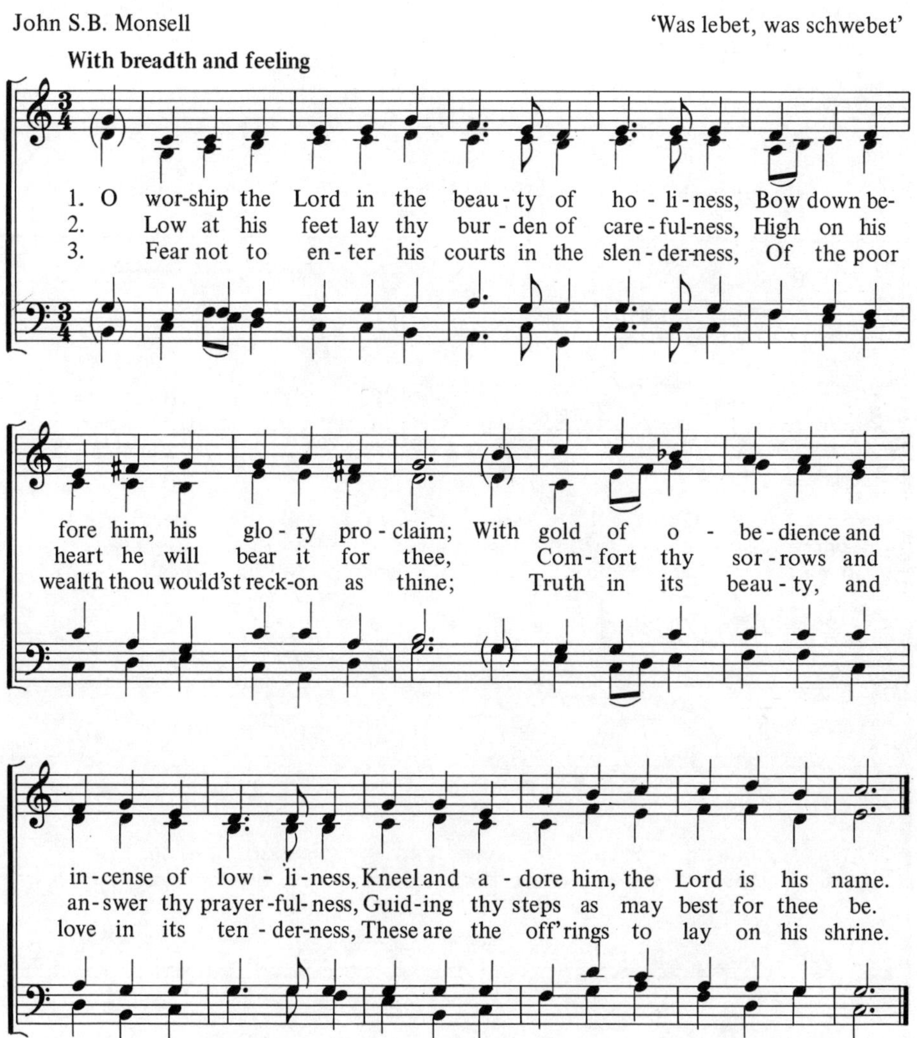
John S.B. Monsell
'Was lebet, was schwebet'
With breadth and feeling
1. O wor-ship the Lord in the beau - ty of ho - li - ness, Bow down be-
2. Low at his feet lay thy bur - den of care - ful-ness, High on his
3. Fear not to en - ter his courts in the slen - der-ness, Of the poor
fore him, his glo - ry pro - claim; With gold of o - be - dience and
heart he will bear it for thee, Com- fort thy sor - rows and
wealth thou would'st reck-on as thine; Truth in its beau - ty, and
in-cense of low - li-ness, Kneel and a - dore him, the Lord is his name.
an-swer thy prayer-ful-ness, Guid-ing thy steps as may best for thee be.
love in its ten - der-ness, These are the off'rings to lay on his shrine.

4. These, though we bring them in trembling and fearfulness,
   He will accept for the name that is dear;
   Mornings of joy give for evenings of tearfulness,
   Trust for our trembling, and hope for our fear.

5. O worship the Lord . . . . *(same as verse 1)*

28. My Jesus, I love thee

Capo 1 (E)
W. R. Featherston — A. J. Gordon

Soft and intense
(E)* (A) (E) (B7) (E)
1. My Je - sus, I love thee, I know thou art mine, For
2. I love thee be - cause thou hast first lov - ed me, And
3. I'll love thee in life, I will love thee in death, And
(A) (E) (B7) (E)
thee all the fol - lies of sin I re - sign. My
pur - chased my par - don on Cal - va - ry's tree. I
praise thee as long as thou lend - est me breath; And
(A) (E) (C♯m) (B7) (E) (A) (E) (B7)
gra - cious Re - deem - er, my Sa - viour art thou:
love thee for wear - ing the thorns on thy brow:
say when the death - dew lies cold on my brow:
If
(E) (A) (E) (C♯m) (B7) (E)
ev - er I loved thee, my Je - sus, 'tis now.

* Guitar chords and 4-part harmonization not designed to be used together.

4. In mansions of glory and endless delight,
I'll ever adore thee in heaven so bright;
I'll sing with the glittering crown on my brow;
If ever I loved thee, my Jesus, 'tis now.

29. Turn your eyes upon Jesus

Capo 1 (E)

H. H. Lemmel

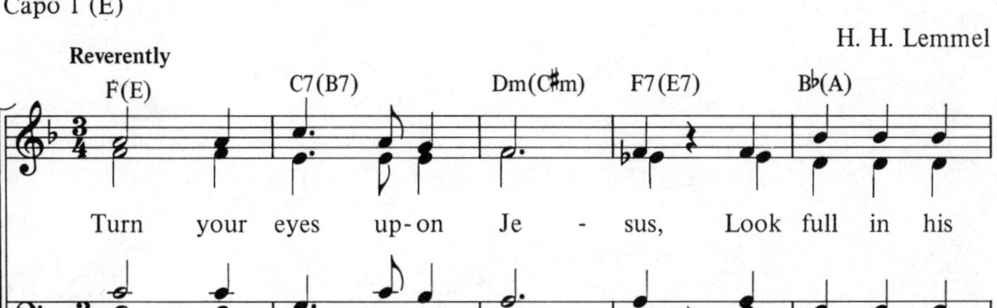

Reverently
F(E)
C7(B7)
Dm(C#m)
F7(E7)
Bb(A)
Turn your eyes up-on Je - sus, Look full in his

C7(B7)
F(E)
F7(E7)
won-der - ful face; And the things of earth will grow

Dm(C#m)
Bb(A)
F(E)
C7(B7)
F(E)
strange- ly dim In the light of his glo - ry and grace.

30. Jesus, the very thought of thee

Tr. Edward Caswall

'Windsor'
M. William Damon
Descant by Betty Pulkingham

With awe; not slow
3. O hope of ev' - ry con - trite heart, O joy of all the meek, To those who fall, how kind thou art, how good to those, to those who seek!
5. Je - sus, our only joy be thou, as thou our prize wilt be, In thee be all our glo - ry now and thro' e - ter - ni - ty.
1. Je - sus, the ve - ry thought of thee With sweet-ness fills the breast; But sweet-er far thy face to see, And in thy pre - sence rest.
2. No voice can sing, no heart can frame, Nor can the mem-ory find, A sweet-er sound than Je - sus' name, The Sa - viour of man - kind.
3. O hope of ev' - ry con - trite heart, O joy of all the meek, To those who fall, how kind thou art! How good to those who seek!

4. But what to those who find? Ah, this
   Nor tongue nor pen can show;
   The love of Jesus, what it is,
   None but who love him know.

5. Jesus, our only joy be thou,
   As thou our prize wilt be;
   In thee be all our glory now,
   And through eternity.

31. My God, how wonderful thou art

Frederick William Faber

'Windsor'
M. William Damon

1. My God, how wonderful thou art,
   Thy majesty how bright!
   How beautiful thy mercy-seat,
   In depths of burning light!

2. How dread are thine eternal years,
   O everlasting Lord,
   By prostrate spirits day and night
   Incessantly adored!

3. O how I fear thee, living God,
   With deepest tenderest fears,
   And worship thee with trembling hope,
   And penitential tears.

4. Yet I may love thee too, O Lord,
   Almighty as thou art,
   For thou hast stooped to ask of me
   The love of my poor heart.

5. How wonderful, how beautiful,
   The sight of thee must be,
   Thine endless wisdom, boundless power,
   And aweful purity.

liturgical songs

Praise the Lord!
Praise the Lord with trumpet and
harp. Praise him with
tambourines and dance.
stringed instruments
and horns.
Let everything praise the Lord!
ruth

SECTION 3

LITURGICAL SONGS

INTROIT

32. Come and dine

C. B. Widmeyer
Arr. Betty Pulkingham

Cheerfully
A D Bm
1. Je - sus has a ta - ble spread where the saints of God are fed, he in-
2. The dis - ci - ples came to land, thus o - bey - ing Christ's com-mand, for the
3. Soon the Lamb will take his bride to be ev - er at his side, all the
E7 A
vites his cho - sen peo - ple, 'Come and dine.' With his
mas - ter called to them, 'Oh come and dine.' There they
host of hea - ven will as - sem - bled be. Oh, 'twill
D Bm
man - na he doth feed and sup - plies our ev' - ry need, oh, 'tis
found their heart's de - sire, bread and fish up - on the fire. Thus he
be a glo - rious sight, all the saints in spot - less white, and with

E7
A
Refrain
sweet to sup with Je - sus all the time!
sat - is - fies the hun - gry ev' - ry time. 'Come and
Je - sus they will feast e - ter - nal - ly.
E7
A
dine,' the mas - ter call - eth. 'Come and dine.' You may
D
B7
E
feast at Je - sus' ta - ble all the time. He who
A
D
Bm
fed the mul - ti - tude, turned the wa - ter in - to wine, to the
E7
A
hun - gry call - eth now, 'Come and dine.'

33. I will arise

Capo 3 (A)

Mimi Farra

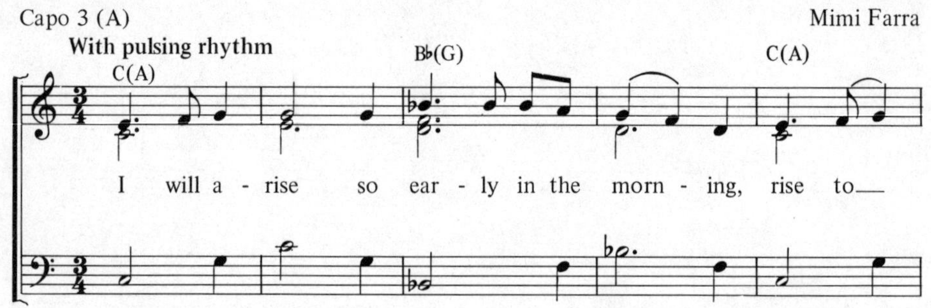
With pulsing rhythm
C(A)
B♭(G)
C(A)
I will a - rise so ear - ly in the morn - ing, rise to

Gm(Em)
C(A)
sing my Sa - viour's prais - es; rise with

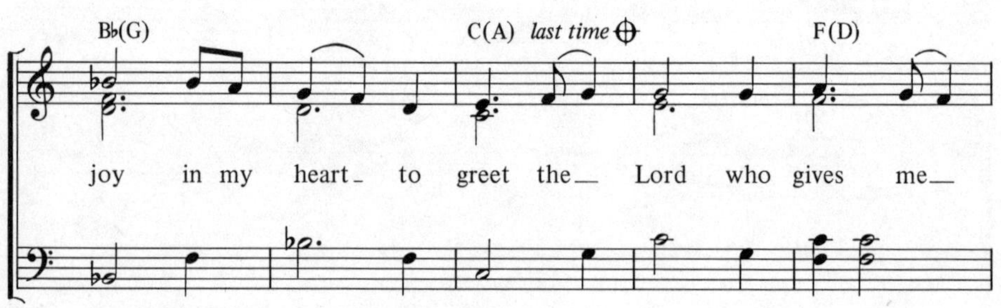
B♭(G)
C(A) last time
F(D)
joy in my heart to greet the Lord who gives me

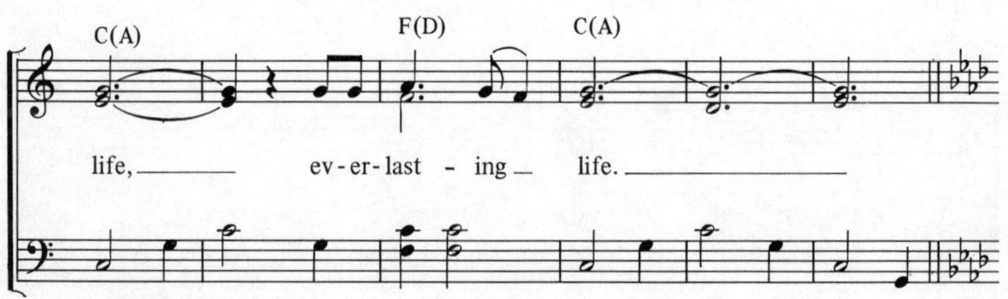
C(A)
F(D)
C(A)
life, ev - er - last - ing life.

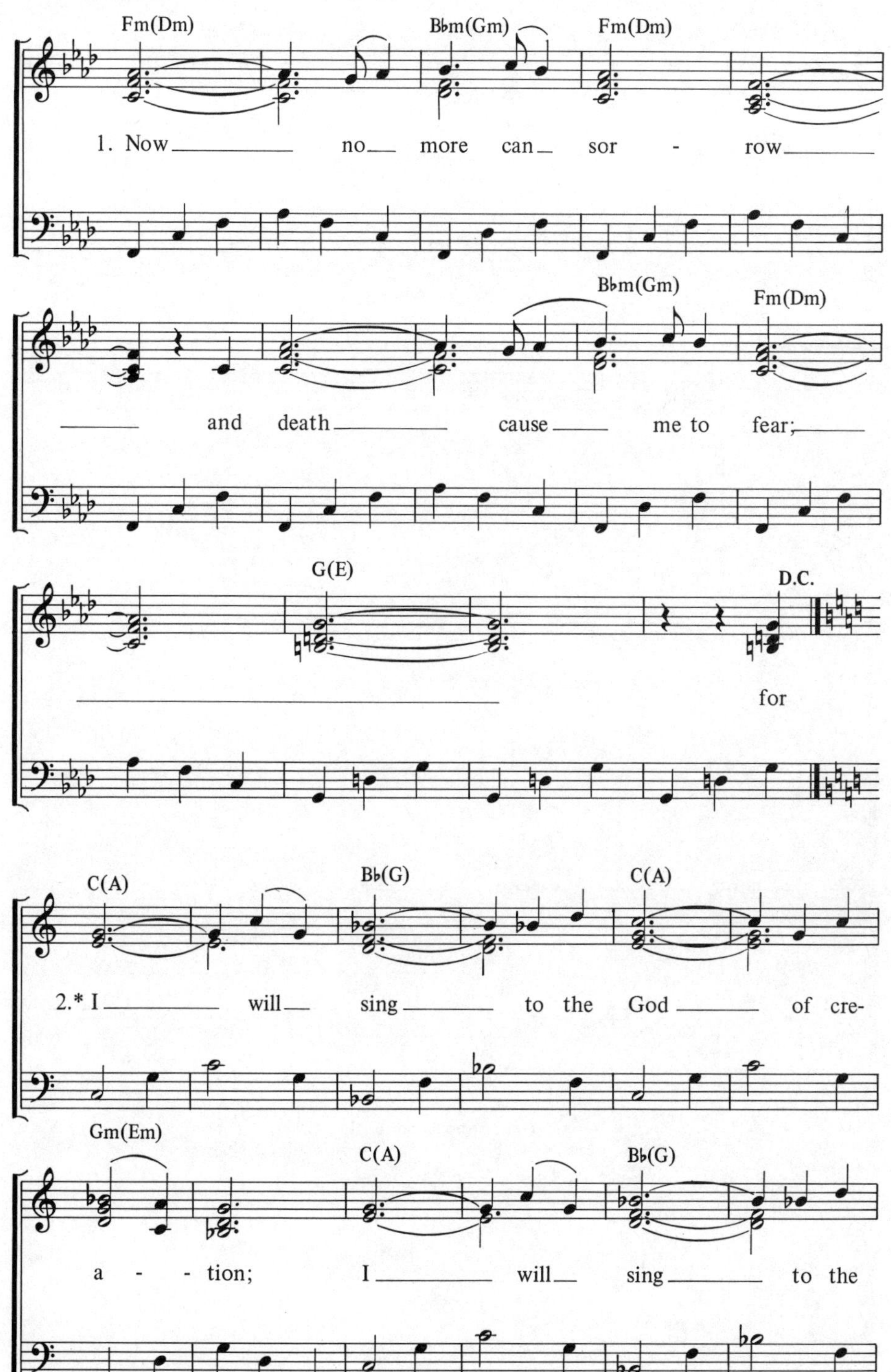
Fm(Dm)
Bbm(Gm)
Fm(Dm)
1. Now no more can sor - row
Bbm(Gm)
Fm(Dm)
and death cause me to fear;
G(E)
D.C.
for
C(A)
Bb(G)
C(A)
2.* I will sing to the God of cre-
Gm(Em)
C(A)
Bb(G)
a - - tion; I will sing to the

C(A)
last time
Gm(Em)
C(A)
D.C.
Lord of love.

last time
F(D)
C(A)
of love, ev-er
Lord who gives me life, ev-er

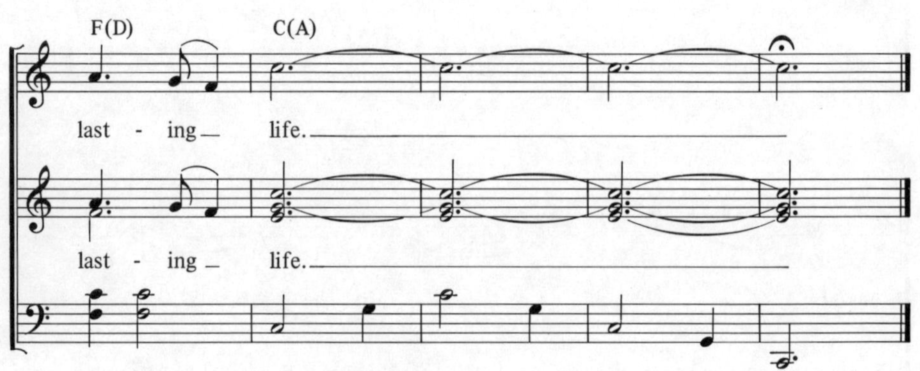
F(D)
C(A)
last - ing life.
last - ing life.

* Verse 2 is a musical complement to the refrain, and the two may be sung together as a final (additional) refrain, using the ending marked *'last time.'*

34. Allelu

Mimi Farra

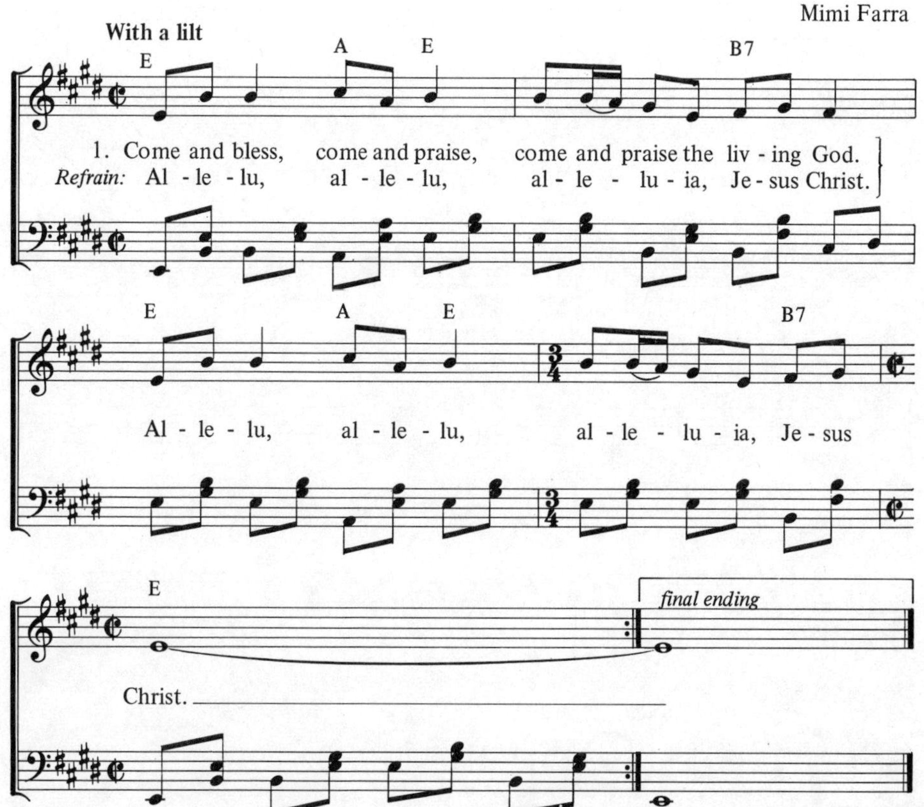
With a lilt
E
A
E
B7
1. Come and bless, come and praise, come and praise the liv - ing God.
Refrain: Al - le - lu, al - le - lu, al - le - lu - ia, Je - sus Christ.
E
A
E
B7
Al - le - lu, al - le - lu, al - le - lu - ia, Je - sus
E
final ending
Christ.

2. Come and seek, come and find, come and find the living God.
   Allelu, allelu, alleluia, Jesus Christ. *Refrain.*

3. Come and hear, come and know, come and know the living God.
   Allelu, allelu, alleluia, Jesus Christ. *Refrain.*

4. Come and bless, come and praise, come and praise the Word of God;
   Word of God, Word made flesh, alleluia, Jesus Christ. *Refrain.*

Seasonal verses:

5. Come behold, come and see, come and see the new-born babe.
   Allelu, allelu, alleluia, Jesus Christ. *Refrain.*

6. Angel choirs sing above, 'Glory to the Son of God!'
   Shepherd folk sing below, 'Allelu, Emmanuel!' *Refrain.*

35. I trust in thee, O Lord

(Psalm 31)

M. Mc Allister
Arr. Jeanne Harper

Smoothly
D
C
D
I trust in thee, O Lord.

F♯m
Bm
Em
I say, 'Thou art my God.'

A7
Bm
F♯m
Em
A7
My times are in thy hand.

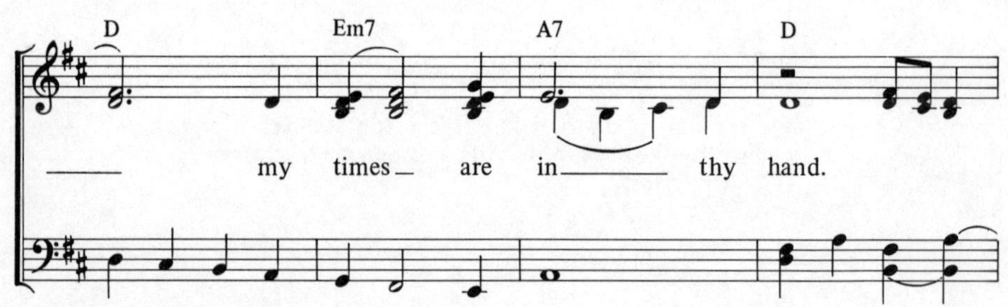
D
Em7
A7
D
my times are in thy hand.

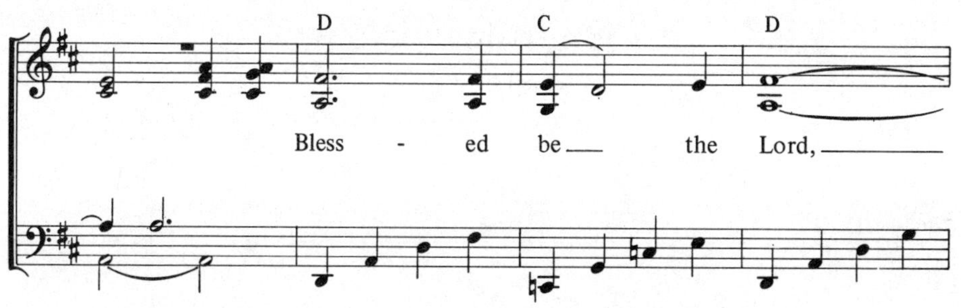
D
C
D
Bless - ed be the Lord,

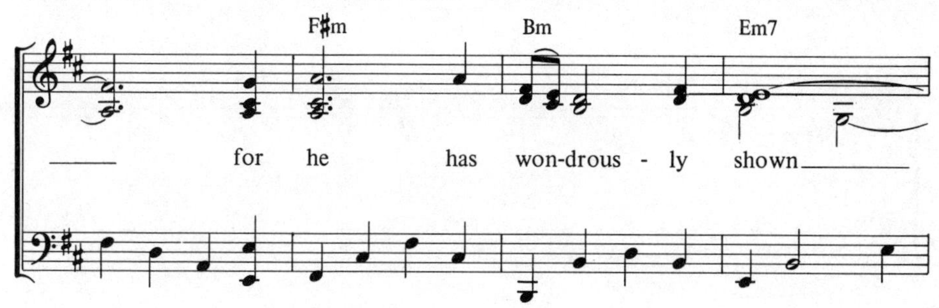
F♯m
Bm
Em7
for he has won-drous - ly shown

A7
Bm7
F♯m
Em
A7
his stead - fast love to me,

D
Em7
A7
D
his stead - fast love to me.

36. O magnify the Lord

(Based on Psalm 34)

Capo 5 (Am)
Ruth Wieting
With an easy rhythmic swing
Dm(Am)
Am7(Em7)
O mag - ni - fy the Lord with
Dm(Am)
Am7(Em7)
me, let us praise
Dm(Am)
Am7 Dm Am7
1. (Em7) (Am) (Em7)
his name to - geth - er. O
2.
Fine
Gm(Dm)
1. I will bless the Lord at
2. I cried un - to the
3. O trust the Lord, you
4. O come, you sons of

Dm(Am) Gm(Dm) Dm(Am)

all times, his praise will al - ways
Lord, and he has freed me
saints, for those who trust him
God, to be the bo - dy

Am7(Em7) Dm(Am) Am7 (Em7) Dm (Am) Am7 (Em7) D.C.

be in my mouth.
from all my fears.
lack no good thing.
of Je - sus Christ.

O

D.C.

37. There is a river

(Psalm 46)

Psalm 46: 4-5

Jonathan Asprey

Fast, rollicking tempo *(1 beat to a bar)*

G
There is a riv - er whose

C Em Am
streams make glad the ci-ty of
G
last time
God, the ci-ty of
Dsus4 D
God; the
G C
ho-ly hab-i-ta-tion of
Em Am G
the most high, the ci-ty of God,

D
G
C
G
Fine
the ci-ty of God.
C
God is in the midst of her,
G
Em
she shall not be moved;
A
A7
the Lord of hosts is
D
D.C.
with her.
For

38. O give thanks unto the Lord

(Psalm 136)

Kathleen Thomerson

Joyfully
Refrain
G
C
O give thanks un-to the Lord, for he is good,
D7
G
for his mer - cy en - dur - eth for - ev - er.

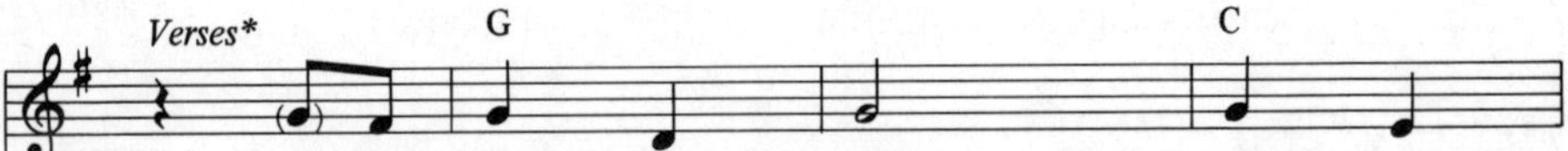

*Verses**

G C

1. O give thanks· un-to the·God of Gods,
O give thanks· un-to the·Lord of Lords,
2. To him· that by·wis - dom made· the heav'ns,
To him·that stretched the·earth a-bove the wa - ter,
3. To him·that smote E - gypt in their· first-born.
And brought out Is-ra-el from a - mong them,
4. To him· which di -·vi - ded the Red Sea,
And made Is· - ra - el to·pass through the midst· of it,
5. To him· which led his·peo-ple through the wil· - der-ness,
To him which smote great kings,
6. Who re - mem - bered us in our low· es - tate,
And hath· re-deemed us from our en· - e - mies,

Christmas Antiphon

7. Al - le - lu - ia, Al - le - lu - ia,
Un - to us· is born a·Son, Al - le - lu - ia,

Fine

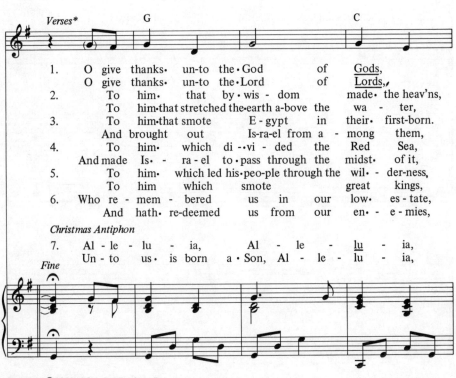

D
G
For his mer - cy en - dur - eth for - ev - er.
D
G
1. To him who a - lone do - eth great won-
2. To him that made great
3. With a strong hand and with a stretched out
4. But ov - er - threw Pha - roah and all his
5. And gave them land for an her - i -
6. O give thanks un - to the God of hea - - -
7. And he shall rule with e - qui -
D
G
3
Refrain
ders,
lights,
arm,
host,
tage,
ven,
ty,
For his mer - cy en - dur - eth for - ev - er.
3
D.C.

*1. Underlined syllables are sung on more than one melody note.
2. A dot (•) shows where to change melody note.

39. The song of Simeon

(Nunc Dimittis)

Capo 3 (E)

Luke 2: 29-32

Mimi Farra

Gently

G(E) G sus4 (E sus4)

Lord, you have ful - filled your word;

G(E) F(D)

now let your ser - vant de - part ___ in

G sus4 (E sus4) (G sus4(E sus4) G (E)

G(E) 1. 2. *fine*

peace. ___ ___

C(A) G(E)

1. With my own eyes ___ I ___ have seen ___ the sal - va - tion, which
2. A ___ light to re - veal ___ you (𝄽) to ___ the na - tions, and the

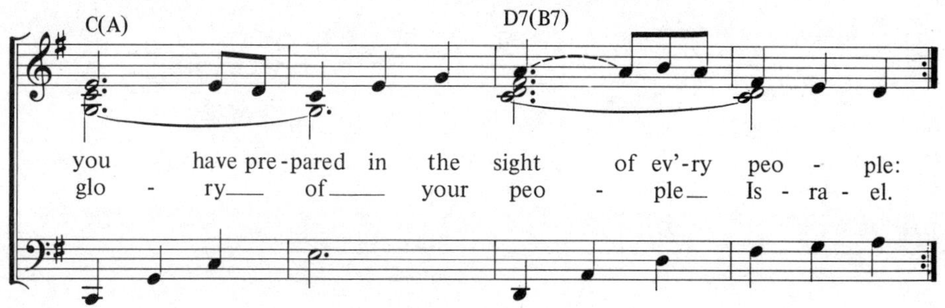
C(A)
D7(B7)
you have pre-pared in the sight of ev'-ry peo - ple:
glo - ry of your peo - ple Is - ra - el.

40. My soul doth magnify the Lord

(Magnificat)

Luke 1: 46-47, 49.

Composer and author unknown
Arr. Betty Pulkingham

Gently

D A7 D

My soul doth mag-ni-fy the Lord, and my

A7

spi - rit hath re-joiced in God my sa - viour for

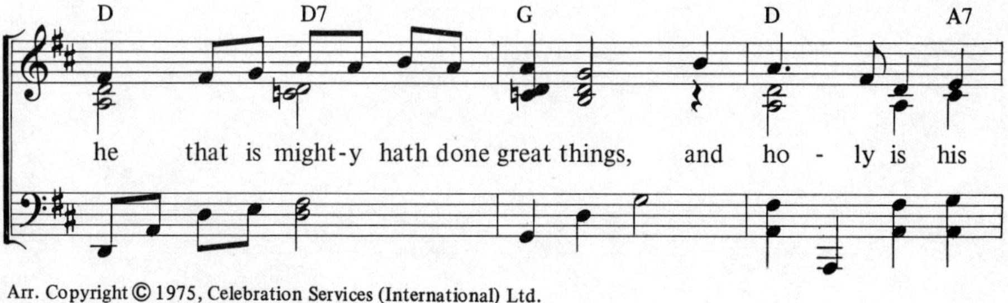

D D7 G D A7

he that is might-y hath done great things, and ho - ly is his

D
A
name. My soul doth mag - ni - fy the Lord, my soul doth
D
E
E7
mag - ni - fy the Lord, and my spi - rit hath re - joiced in God my
A
D
D7
sa - viour for he that is might - y hath done
G
D
A7
great things, and ho - ly is his
D
D
1.
2.
name. My soul doth name.

41. Jesus, Lamb of God

(Agnus Dei)

From *'Mass for the King of Glory'*
Betty Pulkingham
Slow and sustained
D
Bm
Em
Je - sus, Lamb of God, have mer - cy on us.
A
D
Bm
Je - sus, bear-er of our sins, have mer - cy on us.
Em
A
D
Je - sus, re-deem-er of the world, give us your peace.
Bm
Em
A
D
Bm
G
A
D
1.
2.
Give us your peace.

The publishers are grateful to the International Consultation on English Texts for the use of their copyright material.

42. Calypso Doxology

Thomas Ken
Verse 2 - Deanna Wheeler

'Jamaica Farewell'
Lord Burgess
Arr. Betty Pulkingham

With an easy swing
A
D
1. Praise God from whom all bless-ings flow,_ praise him
2. Hal - le - lu - jah! Got the vic - to - ry
3. A - men, a - men, a - men, a - men,_ a - men,
A
E7
A
all ye crea - tures_ here be - low._
o - ver Sa - tan and o - ver sin._
a - men, a - men, a - men, a - men._
A
D
Praise him a - bove, ye_ heav'n - ly host,_ praise him
(𝄾) Je - sus Christ is a - live to - day_ and he
A - men, a - men, a - men, a - men,_ a - men,

A
E7
A
final ending
Fa - ther, Son and Ho - ly Ghost.
leads and guides me all the way.
a - men, a - men, a - men, a - men.

43. Tallis' Canon

Thomas Tallis
'Evening Hymn'

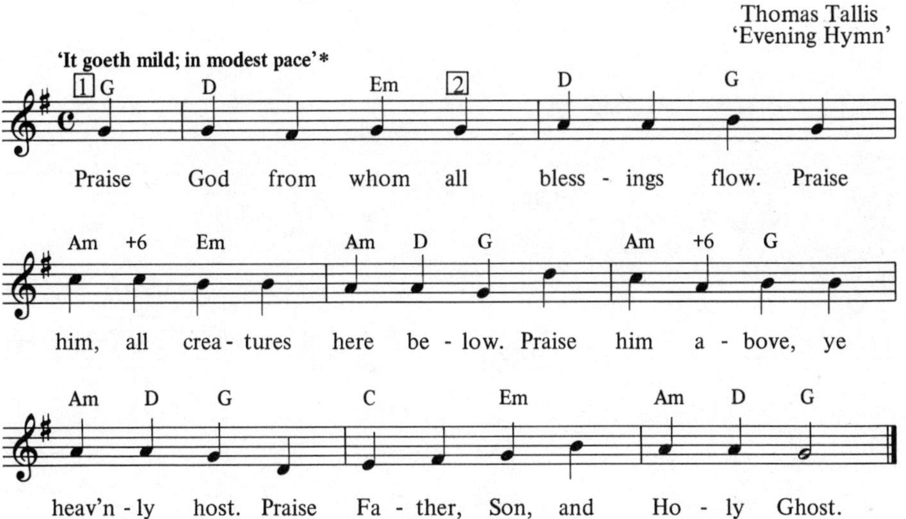
'It goeth mild; in modest pace'*
1 G
D
Em
2
D
G
Praise God from whom all bless - ings flow. Praise
Am +6 Em Am D G Am +6 G
him, all crea - tures here be - low. Praise him a - bove, ye
Am D G C Em Am D G
heav'n - ly host. Praise Fa - ther, Son, and Ho - ly Ghost.

Archbishop Parker's Psalter, c. 1567

44. Doxology

Thomas Ken — Jimmy Owens

With movement
E
G♯m
A
Praise God from whom all bless - ings
E
A
E
B7
flow; Praise him all crea - tures here be-
E
G♯m
A
low. Praise him a - bove ye hea - ven-ly
E
A
E
B7
E
hosts; Praise Fa - ther, Son, and Ho - ly Ghost.

Optional 4-part setting

†
E G♯m A E
Praise God from whom all bless - ings flow; Praise
A E B7 E
him all crea - tures here be - low. Praise
G♯m A E
him a - bove ye hea - ven- ly host; Praise
Praise him
A E B7 E E
1, 2. final ending
Fa - ther, Son, and Ho - ly Ghost. Praise Ghost.

† One very attractive way to sing this song in parts:

First time:	Sopranos begin	Add altos at mid-point*
Second time:	Tenors join	Basses too (at mid-point)*
Third time:	All sing	

45. The Lord's Prayer

Jodi Page

Slow and sustained
D
D Maj7
Am7
Our Fa - ther in hea-ven, hal-lowed be your
G
A
name. Your king-dom come, your will be done on
G
D
earth as in hea-ven.
D Maj7
Am7
Give us to-day our dai-ly bread. For-give us our
G
A
G
sins as we for-give those who sin a-

D
cresc.
gainst us.
Do not bring us to the
D Maj7
Am7
time of trial
but de-liv-er us from
8
G
D
D Maj7
e - vil. For the king - dom, the pow - er, and the
Am7
G
glo - ry are yours now and for-
A
A7
slowly
D
ev - er. A - - men.

46. Hallowed be thy name

Traditional
Arr. Betty Pulkingham

With childlike simplicity

G
D7
G
D7
1. Our Fa - ther who art in hea - ven,
2. On the earth as it is in hea - ven,
3. give us all our tres - pas - ses,
4. lead us not to the de - vil to be tempt - ed,
5. thine is the king-dom and the pow- er and the glo - ry,
6. men, a - men, a - men, a - men,

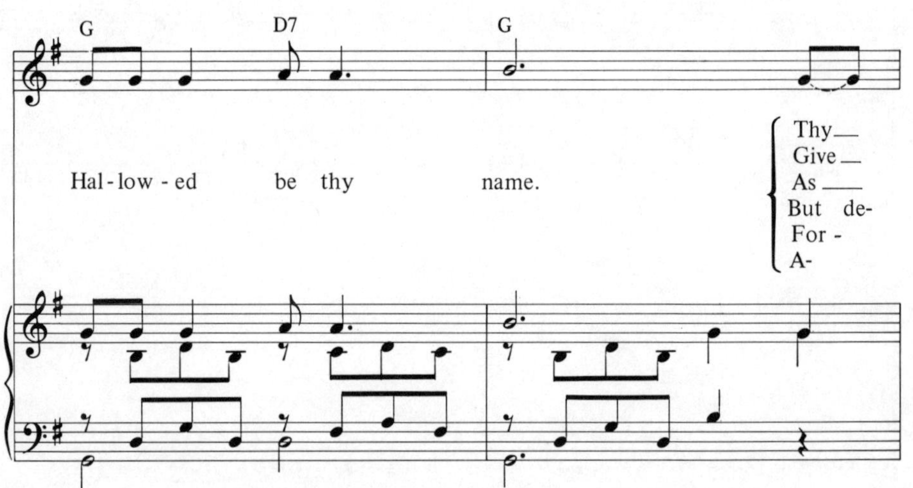
G
D7
G
Hal - low - ed be thy name.
Thy
Give
As
But de-
For -
A-

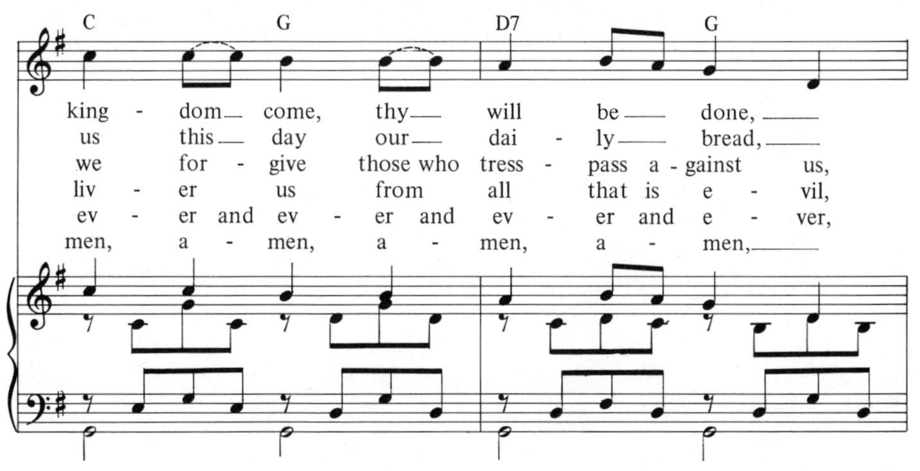
C
G
D7
G
king - dom come, thy will be done,
us this day our dai - ly bread,
we for - give those who tress - pass a - gainst us,
liv - er us from all that is e - vil,
ev - er and ev - er and ev - er and e - ver,
men, a - men, a - men, a - men,

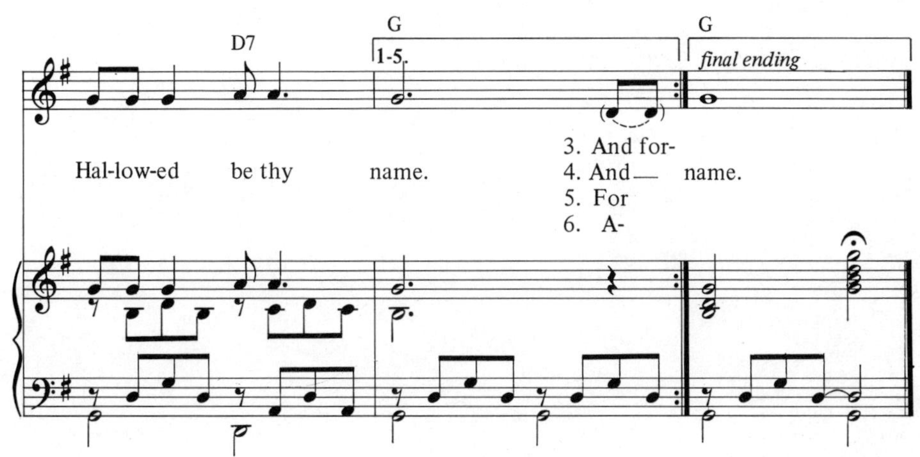
D7
G
G
1-5.
final ending
Hal-low-ed be thy name.
3. And for-
4. And name.
5. For
6. A-

become...

ruth

ongs of wholeness and maturity

47. The steadfast love of the Lord

Capo 4 (C)

Edith Mc Neill

With a rocking rhythm
Refrain E(C)*
A(F)
E(C)
The stead-fast love of the Lord nev-er ceas - es; his mer-cies
A(F)
B(G)
A(F)
F#m(Dm)
nev - er come to an end. They are new ev'-ry morn-ing,
G#m(Em)
C#m(Am)
F#m(Dm7)
B(G)
E(C) B(G) E(C)
new ev'-ry morn-ing. Great is thy faith - ful - ness, O Lord!
A(F)
B(G)
E(C)
Vss. 2-4
Fine
A(F)
Great is thy faith-ful - ness. 1. The Lord is my por-tion, says my

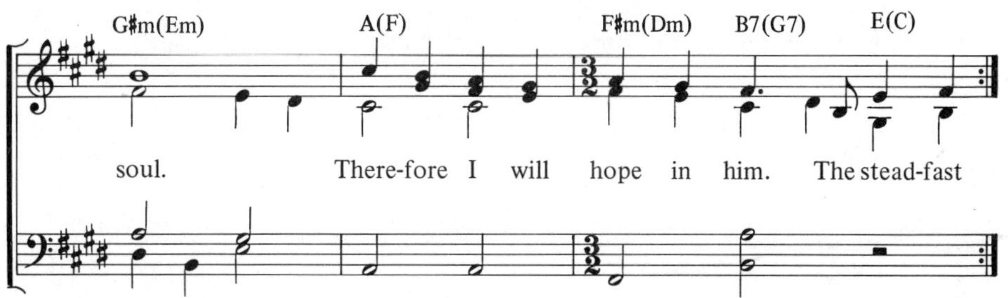
G♯m(Em)
A(F)
F♯m(Dm)
B7(G7)
E(C)
soul. There-fore I will hope in him. The stead-fast

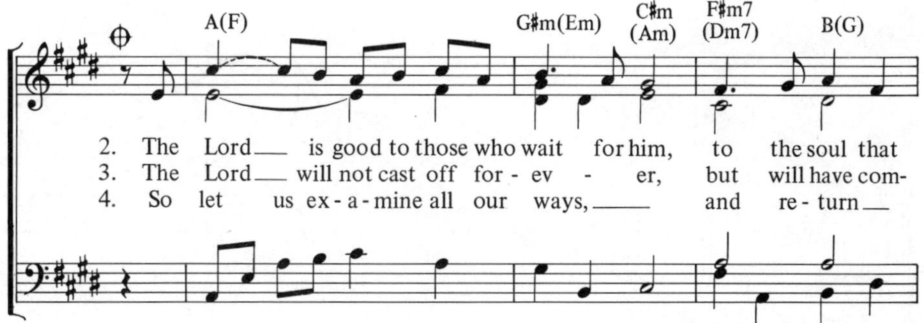
A(F)
G♯m(Em)
C♯m (Am)
F♯m7 (Dm7)
B(G)
2. The Lord is good to those who wait for him, to the soul that
3. The Lord will not cast off for - ev - er, but will have com-
4. So let us ex - a - mine all our ways, and re - turn

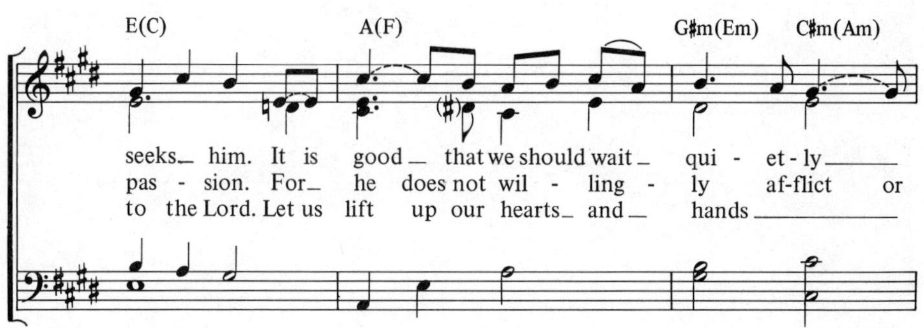
E(C)
A(F)
G♯m(Em)
C♯m(Am)
seeks him. It is good that we should wait qui - et - ly
pas - sion. For he does not wil - ling - ly af-flict or
to the Lord. Let us lift up our hearts and hands

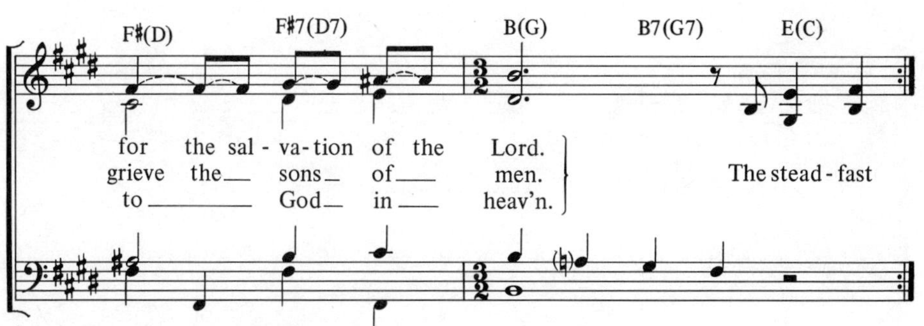
F♯(D)
F♯7(D7)
B(G)
B7(G7)
E(C)
for the sal - va - tion of the Lord.
grieve the sons of men.
to God in heav'n.
The stead - fast

*Guitar chords and piano arrangement not designed to be used together.

48. Put on love

Col. 3: 12-16

Jodi Page

Folk-rock
Refrain
E
A
Put
on
E
1.
love,
E
2.
love.
And the
A
B7
E
peace of God
that binds us
all
to-geth - er

A
will keep our hearts in

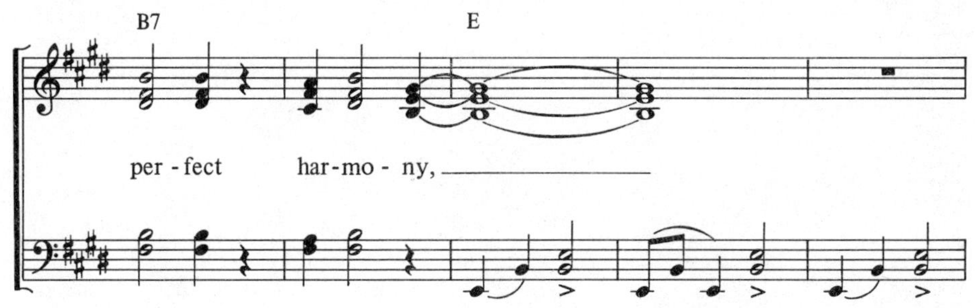
B7
E
per - fect har-mo - ny,

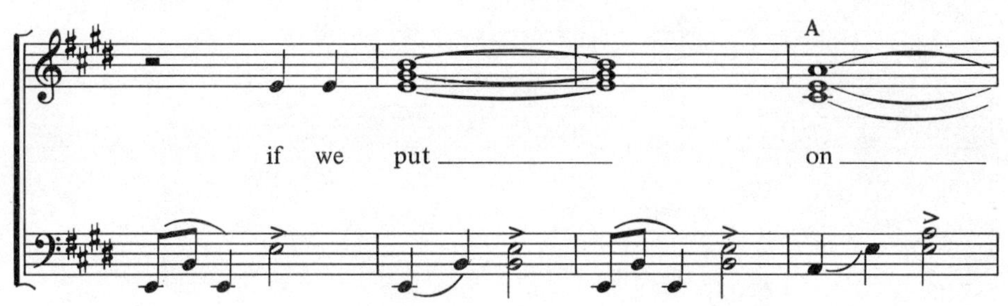
A
if we put
on

E
last time
love.

A
1. We are God's cho - sen race, his
2. God has for - giv - en us, now
3. Al - ways be thank - ful and
B7
E
saints, and he loves us.
we should for - give our bro - ther.
let the mes - sage of Je - - - sus
A
We should be clothed in peace, in
We should show gen - tle - ness and
in all its rich-ness find a

B7
E
D.C.
kind - ness, and hu - mi - li - ty As we
bear with one an - oth - er As we
dwell-ing place in our hearts As we
E
dim.
A
Put
on
E
love.

49. I heard the voice of Jesus say

Horatius Bonar

'Kingsfold'
Traditional English melody
Arr. Betty Pulkingham

Flowing
Em Am (+6) Em D G Am
1. I___ heard the voice of Je - sus say, 'Come un - to me_ and
heard the voice of Je - sus say, 'Be - hold, I free - ly
heard the voice of Je - sus say, 'I___ am this dark world's
*
D C D Em D
rest; Lay_ down, thou wea - ry one, lay down Thy_
give The_ liv - ing wa - ter; thirst - y one, Stoop
light; Look un - to me, thy morn shall rise, And_
l.h.
G Am Em Bm7 Em
head up - on_ my breast.' I___ came to Je - sus
down and drink, and live.' I___ came to Je - sus
all thy day_ be bright.' I___ looked to Je - sus

Am (+6) Em C Maj7 D
as I was, Wea - ry and worn and sad; I
and I drank Of that life - giv - ing stream; My
and I found In him my star, my sun; And
C D G D G Am
found in him a rest - ing place, And he has made me
thirst was quenched, my soul re - vived, And now I live in
in that light of life I'll walk 'Til trav' - ling days are
Em
1-2.
3.
glad.
him.
done.
2. I
3. I
Rit. and dim.

*The obligato (stems up) may be played by a flute or by a solo stop on the organ.

50. There is power in the blood

Verses: Gary Miles
Refrain: L. E. Jones

Verses: Gary Miles
Refrain: L. E. Jones

With warmth and tenderness
G
D7
1. My Je - sus, he saves and heals me, my
2. He fills me to o - ver flow - ing, he
3. Our Fa - ther, he made and loves us, he
C
D7
G
bo - - - - - - - dy, spi - rit, soul. My
comes as the dove, My
gave his on - ly son. We'll
G7
C
Am
king and my shep- herd leads me and
spi - rit and his u - ni - ted. Oh,
see him one day in glo - ry and
D
D7
G
Refrain
makes my bo - dy whole.
won - - - - - - drous, pre-cious love. Oh, there is
join the Three in One.

G G7 C G
power, power, won - der - work - ing power in the
D D7 G G7
blood of the Lamb. There is power, power,
C G D7 G
won -der work-ing power in the pre - cious blood of the Lamb.

51. The man of Galilee

Linda Rich
Arr. Betty Pulkingham

With an easy swing

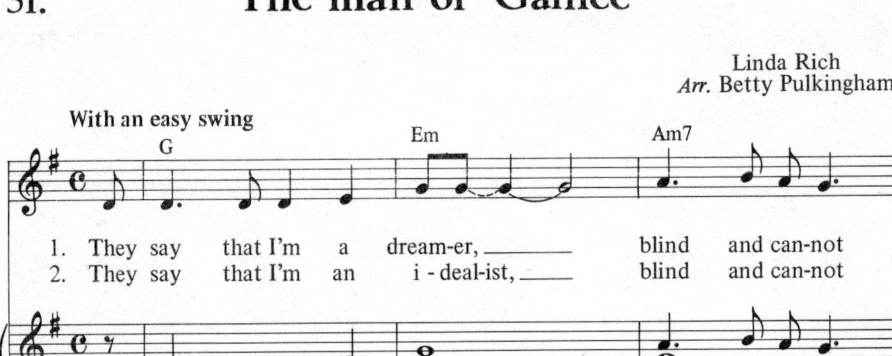
G
Em
Am7
1. They say that I'm a dream-er, blind and can-not
2. They say that I'm an i-deal-ist, blind and can-not

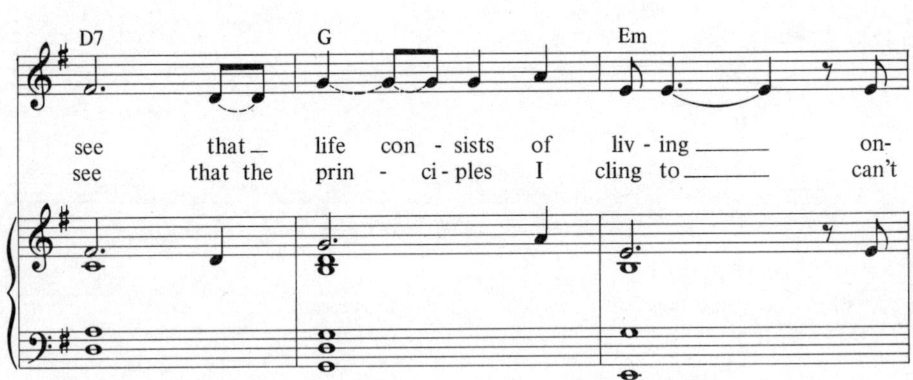
D7
G
Em
see that life con-sists of liv-ing on-
see that the prin-ci-ples I cling to can't

Am7
D
G
ly to earn mon-ey. Well, you know who I
stand re-a-li-ty. Well, I know who you

Em Am7 D7 G
am, Lord;
are, Lord;
you'll al - ways care for me. I on - ly want to
Em Am D7 G
be like the man of Gal - i - lee.
Refrain D7 G G7
I want to be walk like, I want to
C G
hear talk like, I want to see be like the
1. D7 2. D7 G Fine
man of Gal - i - man of Gal - i - lee.

52. Wind, wind

Jane and Betsy Clowe — Jane Clowe

Smooth and sustained

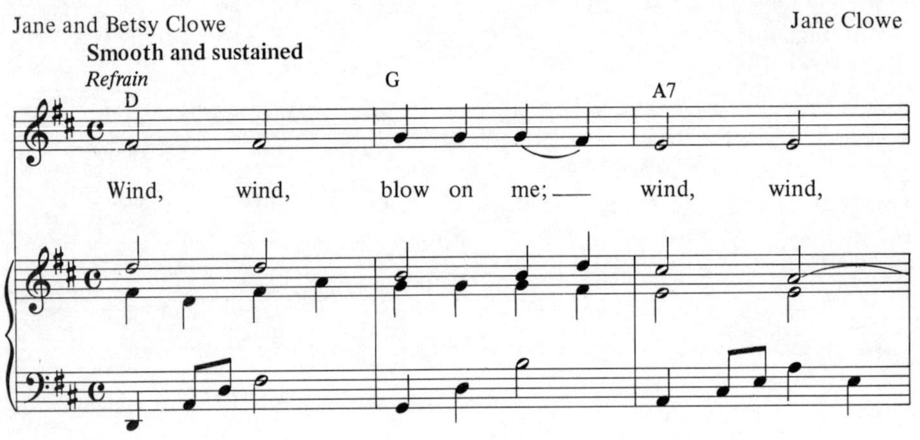
Refrain
D
G
A7
Wind, wind, blow on me; wind, wind,

D
G
Em
set me free; wind, wind, my Fa - ther sent the

A7
G
D
last time
bless - ed Ho - ly Spi - rit.

D G A7
1. Je - sus told us all a - bout you, how we could not
2. When we're wea - ry you con - sole us; when we're lone - ly
3. When un - to the Church you came, it was not in your own but
4. Set us free to love our bro - thers; set us free to
D G
live with - out you, with his blood the
you en - fold us; when in dan - ger
Je - sus' name. Je - sus Christ is
live for oth - ers that the world the
Em A7 D D.C.
pow - er bought to help us live the life he taught.
you up - hold us, bless - ed Ho - ly Spi - rit.
still the same, he sends the Ho - ly Spi - rit.
Son might see and Je - sus' name ex - alt - ed be.
D.C.

53. The fruit of the Spirit

Capo 1 (E)
Refrain: Gal. 5: 22-23

Brian Casebow

Flowing
Refrain
F(E) Bb(A) F(E)
For the fruit of the Spi-rit is love, joy, peace, pa-tience, kind-ness,
Bb(A) C7(B7) F(E) Dm(C#m) Bb(A) F(E)
good - ness, faith-ful-ness, gen-tle-ness, self - con - trol; for
Bb(A) C7(B7) F(E) Fine Gm(F#m)
such there is no law.
1. Have you seen my Lord on the
2. Have you seen his face and the
3. Can we an - swer him? Can the
Dm(C#m) C7(B7) F(E)
cross so high? Do you know his name? Do you hear his cry? 'Fa-ther,
look he gave to the dy - ing man he a - lone would save? 'Sin-ner,
heart re - ply? How to fol - low him as we live and die! 'Je - sus,
Gm(F#m) Dm(C#m) Gm(F#m) C7(B7) F(E)
here's my love. Fa-ther, take my love, as the tree bears fruit for you'.
here's my love. Sin-ner, take my love, as the tree bears fruit for you'.
here's our love. Je- sus, take our love, as the tree bears fruit for you'.

54. By their fruits ye shall know them

Capo 3 (C)
Based on Matt. 7: 16

Jon Wilkes
Arr. Betty Pulkingham

With quiet simplicity
Refrain
Eb(C)
Ab(F)
Eb(C)
Can men gath-er grapes from the thorns, or
(mel.)
Fm(Dm)
Bb(G)
figs from the thistl - ed stem?
Eb(C)
Gm(Em)
Cm(Am)
v. 3 (solo) Fa - ther, for - give, they know not what they do;
He that hath ears let him hear,

Ab(F)
Bb(G)
Eb(C)
last time
by their fruits ye shall know them.
last time
Verses
Eb(C)
Gm(Em)
Cm(Am)
1. My friend came to man to show him how to love; his
2. In dark-ness they led him to priests and kings, they
3. They nailed his hands and split his side, they
4. Bro-thers, oh, judge the heart of man-kind, the
(hum)
Ab(F)
Bb(G)
bless-ing he gave to the meek. But
called him the Lord of the flies.
cast the lots for his clothes.
test is sure and true.

E♭(C)
Gm(Em)
Cm(Am)
men took his love and they called it a lie, his
Spat in his face and they crowned him with thorns:
The on - ly com-fort they had to give was
Eat of the fruit and sa - vour the taste.
A♭(F)
B♭(G)
Refrain
an - swer was on - ly this cry:
'Hail, the King of the Jews.'
vin - - e - gar and gall.
What does it say to you?
A♭(F)
B♭ (G)
E♭(C)
by their fruits ye shall know them.

55. My God

(A psalm of spring)

Capo 1 (E)
Nan Pagano
With warmth
Refrain
F(E) C7(B7) F(E) Bb(A) F(E) C7(B7) F(E) F7(E7) Bb(A) F(E) C7(B7) F(E)
My God makes the flow-ers to bloom. My God sends the rain.
My God sets the rain-bow in the sky, hears each ba-by when he cries, and each mo-ther as she sighs, sent his on - ly Son to die.
Oh, praise him, my God is the on- ly true and liv-ing God and he has made me his child.
Fine

F(E)
C7(B7)
1. One day in spring while walk-ing with the Lord,
world and I have gi - ven it to you, ev' - ry
2. When sum-mer heat re-veals the cir-cum-stance of life, the
comes and all your world is turn-ing brown, the
3. He spoke a - gain and said,'You are a child of mine, a
out, 'I see, it's all a gift from thee! Let the
1.
F(E)
list - 'ning to his word, I heard him say, 'This is my
bur - den and the strife, call on my name. Then aut-umn
branch up - on the vine. Bring forth my fruit.' My heart cried
2.
F(E)
col - our, ev' - ry hue, ev'- ry breeze and drop of dew is from my
leaves are fall-ing down and win-ter's cold is all a - round. It's from my
sea-sons have their way, Lord, walk with me through night and day. It's from your

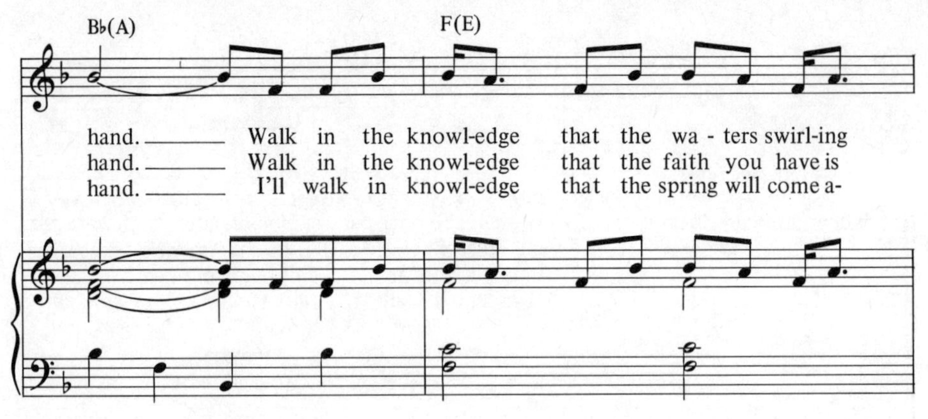
Bb(A)
F(E)
hand. Walk in the knowl-edge that the wa - ters swirl-ing
hand. Walk in the knowl-edge that the faith you have is
hand. I'll walk in knowl-edge that the spring will come a-

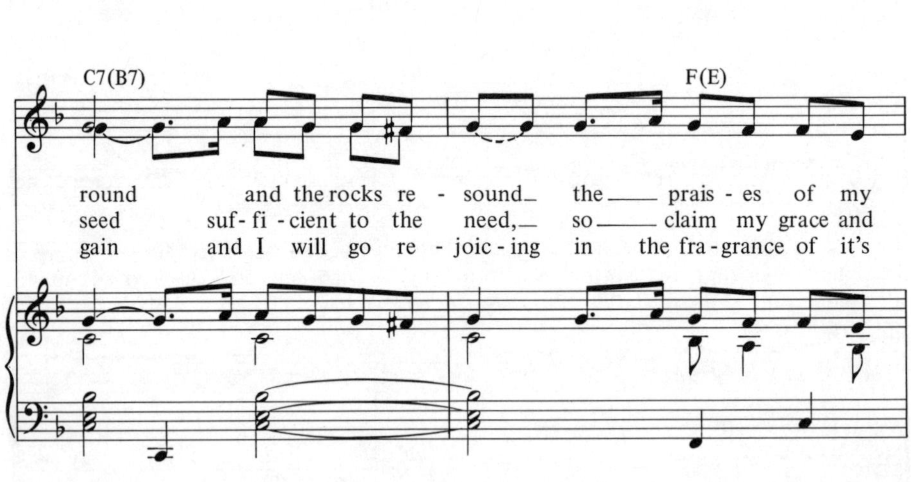
C7(B7)
F(E)
round and the rocks re - sound the prais - es of my
seed suf - fi - cient to the need, so claim my grace and
gain and I will go re - joic - ing in the fra - grance of it's

D.S.
name.
live!'
bloom.'
My heart cried, my God makes the flow-ers to bloom.
D.S.

56. Israel is my vineyard

Isaiah 27 : 2-3
Capo 2 (Em)

Marie Malone

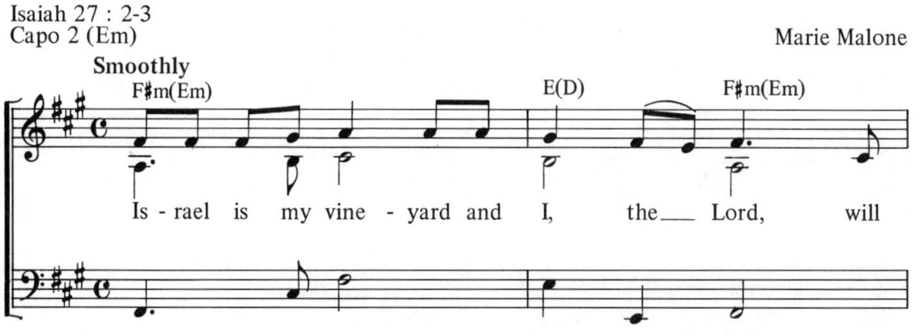
Smoothly
F♯m(Em)
E(D)
F♯m(Em)
Is - rael is my vine - yard and I, the __ Lord, will

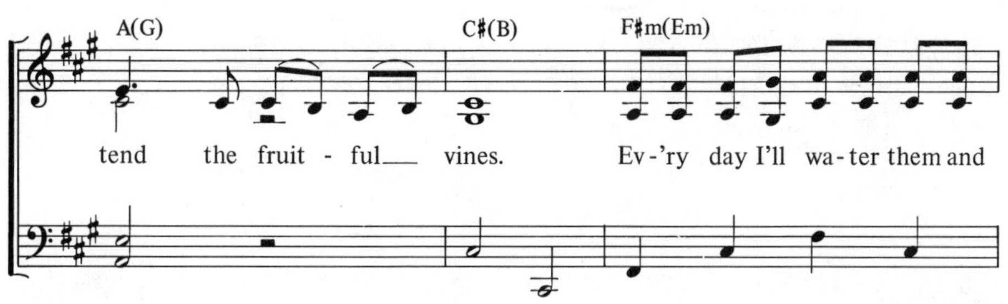
A(G)
C♯(B)
F♯m(Em)
tend the fruit - ful __ vines. Ev -'ry day I'll wa - ter them and

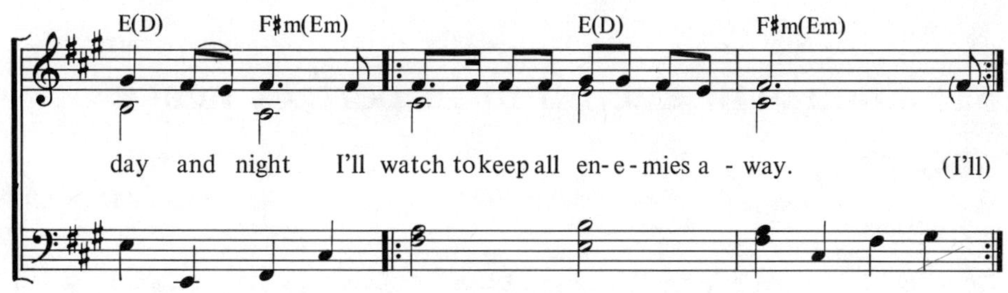
E(D)
F♯m(Em)
E(D)
F♯m(Em)
day and night I'll watch to keep all en - e - mies a - way. (I'll)

F♯m(Em)
E(D)
F♯m(Em)
E(D)
Al - le - lu - ia, al - le - lu - ia, praise the Lord! Al - le - lu - ia, praise his name!

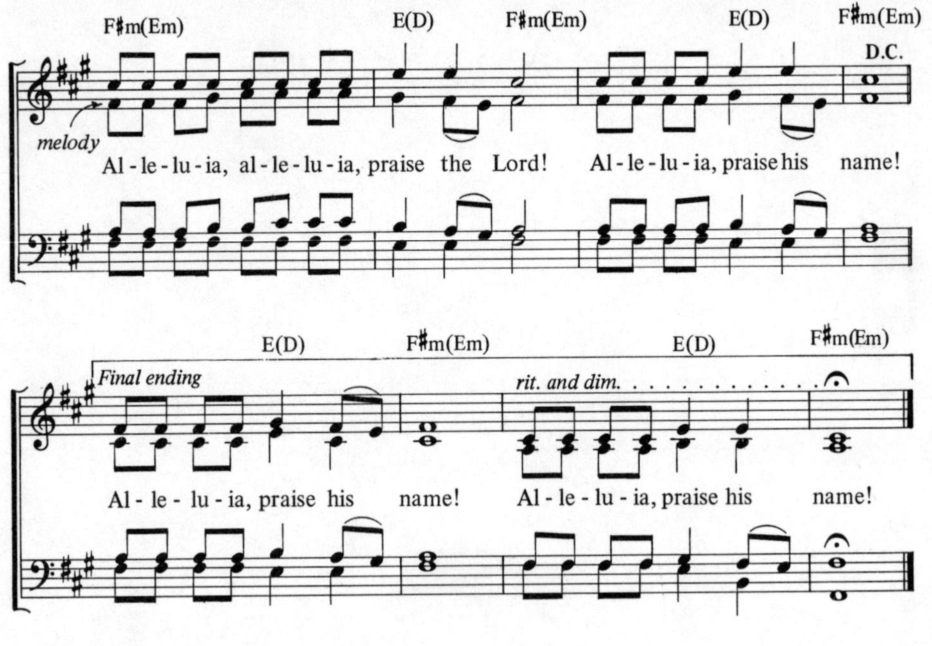

F♯m(Em)
E(D)
F♯m(Em)
E(D)
F♯m(Em)
D.C.
melody
Al - le - lu - ia, al - le - lu - ia, praise the Lord! Al - le - lu - ia, praise his name!
E(D)
F♯m(Em)
E(D)
F♯m(Em)
Final ending
rit. and dim.
Al - le - lu - ia, praise his name! Al - le - lu - ia, praise his name!

57. Thou wilt keep him in perfect peace

Anon.
Arr. Paul Beckwith

Quietly
A
D
A
E
Descant 3. Though your sins as scar - let be, Though your
1. Thou wilt keep him in per - fect peace, Thou wilt keep him in
2. Mar - vel not that I say un - to you, Mar - vel not that I
3. Though your sins as scar - let be, Though your sins as

E7
A
sins as scar - let be, Though your
per - fect peace, Thou wilt keep him in
say un - to you, Mar - vel not that I
scar - let be, Though your sins as
A7
D
A
E
A
sins as scar - let be, They shall be white as snow.
per - fect peace Whose mind is stayed on thee.
say un - to you, Ye must be born a - gain.
scar - let be, They shall be white as snow.

4. If the Son shall make you free,
   If the Son shall make you free,
   If the Son shall make you free,
   Ye shall be free indeed.

5. They that wait upon the Lord,
   They that wait upon the Lord,
   They that wait upon the Lord,
   They shall renew their strength.

6. Whom shall I send and who will go?
   Whom shall I send and who will go?
   Whom shall I send and who will go?
   Here I am, Lord, send me.

songs of the kingdom
(the Body of Christ)

including songs
for Holy Communion

58. The Lord is a great and mighty king

Diane Davis

Lively
Refrain
E
A
E
The Lord is a great and might - y king,
A
B7
just and gen-tle with ev - e - ry thing.
E
A
E
So with hap - pi - ness ___ we sing,

B7
E
1 - 4
E A E
final ending
and let his prais - es ring.
ring.

A
E
1. We are his voice, we his song;
2. We are his bo - dy here on earth;
3. For our Lord we will stand,
4. The Lord our God is one,

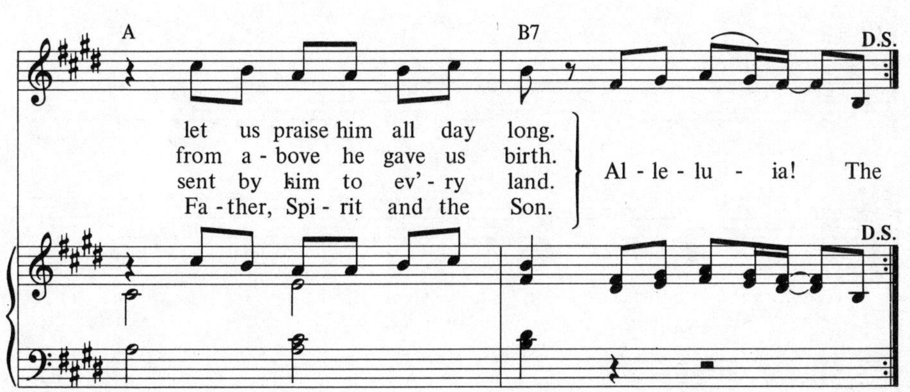
A
B7
D.S.
let us praise him all day long.
from a - bove he gave us birth.
sent by him to ev' - ry land.
Fa - ther, Spi - rit and the Son.
Al - le - lu - ia! The
D.S.

59. This is the feast

John Ylvisaker
Arr. Betty Pulkingham
Majestically
Refrain
F G C G Am
This is the feast of vic-t'ry for our God, for the
Dm G C G Am F G
Lamb who was slain has be-gun his reign: Al - le - lu -
E C Am Dm G C
1-2 3.
ia. ia. 1. Wor - thy is Christ, the Lamb who was slain, whose
2. Sing with all the peo - ple of God and
F G C Am F G
blood set us free to be peo-ple of God. Pow - er, rich - es,
join in the hymn of all cre - a - - - - - tion: 'Bless - ing, hon - our,
Em Am Dm G C Am
wis - dom and strength, and hon - our, bless - ing and glo - ry are his. This
glo - ry and might be to God and the Lamb for - ev - er. A - men.' This

60. Please break this bread, Lord

Jodi Page

Tender and lyrical
Refrain
G
Am7
Please break this bread, Lord,
D
G
please break this bread,
bread of your
Am7
D
G
bo-dy
ris-en in us.
Am7
D
Pour out your wine, Lord,
pour out
G
your wine.
Let it flow

Am7
D
G
last time
through us
to a thirst-y world.
C
D
1. We've come to eat your bread, make us
mem'-ry of your death to give you
2. Let us be bro-ken, O Lord, to feed your
Spi-rit and life that sat-is-
G
C
1.
one. We've come to drink your
thanks. We've come to
sheep. Let us be poured out, O
fy, that you are
D
G
wine, make us one. We've come to
Lord, that men may see that you are

Verse 1
1. C
D
G
D.C.
cel-e - brate your life and give you praise.
D.C.
Verse 2
2C
D
G
D.C.
ris - en in us to set men free.
D.C.
last time
Am7
D
Please break this bread, Lord, please break this
G
Am7
bread. Pour out your wine, Lord,
D
rit.
G
pour out your wine.

61. Let us break bread together

Traditional
Arr. Mimi Farra

Warmly
E F#m G#m F#m E F#m
1. Let us break bread to - geth - er, we are one.
drink wine to - geth - er, we are one.
praise God to - geth - er, we are one.
G#m F#m E B7 E F# B7
Let us break bread to - geth - er, we are one.
Let us drink wine to - geth - er, we are one.
Let us praise God to - geth - er, we are one.
E B7 E E7 A F#m
1-3. We are one as we stand with our face to the ris - en
B7 E F#m G#m F#m E F#m G#m F#m
1-2.
Son. Oh, Lord, have mer-cy on us. 2-3. Let us

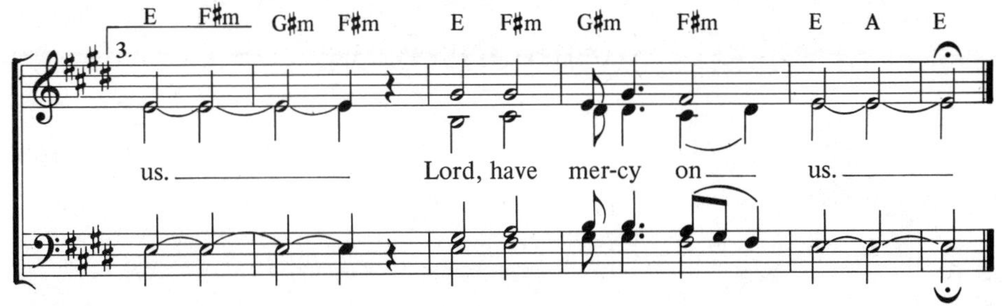
E F♯m G♯m F♯m E F♯m G♯m F♯m E A E
3.
us.
Lord, have mer-cy on us.

62. Who are my mother and my brothers?

Charles High

With deep feeling

An - y - one who does the will of God,

an - y - one who does the will of God,

an - y - one who does the will of God is my bro - ther,

my sis-ter and mo - - - - - ther.

63. Triumphant Zion

Philip Doddridge

Gary Miles

Well-accented, not fast
E
1. Tri - um - phant
2. Put all thy
3. No more shall
4. God from on
G
A
G
Zi - on, lift thy head
beau - teous gar - ments on,
foes un - clean in - vade,
high has heard thy prayer,
E
G
A
From dust and dark - ness and the
And let thine ex - cel - lence be
And fill thy hal - lowed walls with
His hand thy ru - ins shall re-

E
G
dead;
known:
dread;
pair:
Though hum - bled long, a -
Decked in the robes of
No more shall hell's in -
Nor will thy watch - ful
A
E
G
wake at length,
right - eous - ness,
sult - ing host
mon - arch cease
And gird thee with thy
The world thy glo - ries
Their vic - t'ry and thy
To guard thee in e -
A
E
1-3.
4.
Sa - viour's strength.
shall con - fess.
sor - rows boast.
ter - nal peace.

64. What could be better?

Brian Howard

Crisp and bright
C
1. What could be bet-ter than to
2. What could be bet-ter than to
3. What could be bet-ter than to
4. What could be bet-ter than to
F C G C
come_ to dine on this bread_ and on___ this wine, the
car-ry the cross that our Lord_ has giv - en us?
live in love with God's ho - ly cho - sen ones,
fol-low the Lord? In this whole wide world, there's no-thing I'm sure. So
F C G
bread of___ life_ and the cup of suf-fer-ing, the bo-dy and blood_ of
Just like his on - ly be - got - ten_ Son, he's cho - sen us___ to
liv - ing to-geth - er in u - ni - ty, and out of that life___ the
fol - low___ him_ we shall sure - ly___ do. Lis-ten he's speak-ing to

C
Je-sus, our King?
I be-
car - ry one.
I be-
world to feed?
I be-
me and you.
I be-
F
G
C
lieve he's o-pened our eyes to real-ly see there's
lieve he's o-pened our eyes to real-ly see there's
lieve he's o-pened our eyes to real-ly see there's
lieve he's o-pened our eyes to real-ly see there's
F
G
C
noth - ing bet-ter than to come to dine in u - ni - ty.
noth - ing bet-ter than to car-ry the cross in u - ni - ty.
noth - ing bet-ter than to live to-geth-er in u - ni - ty.
noth - ing bet-ter than to fol-low the Lord in u - ni - ty.

65. Guide me, O thou great Jehovah

William Williams

'Cwm Rhondda'
John Hughes

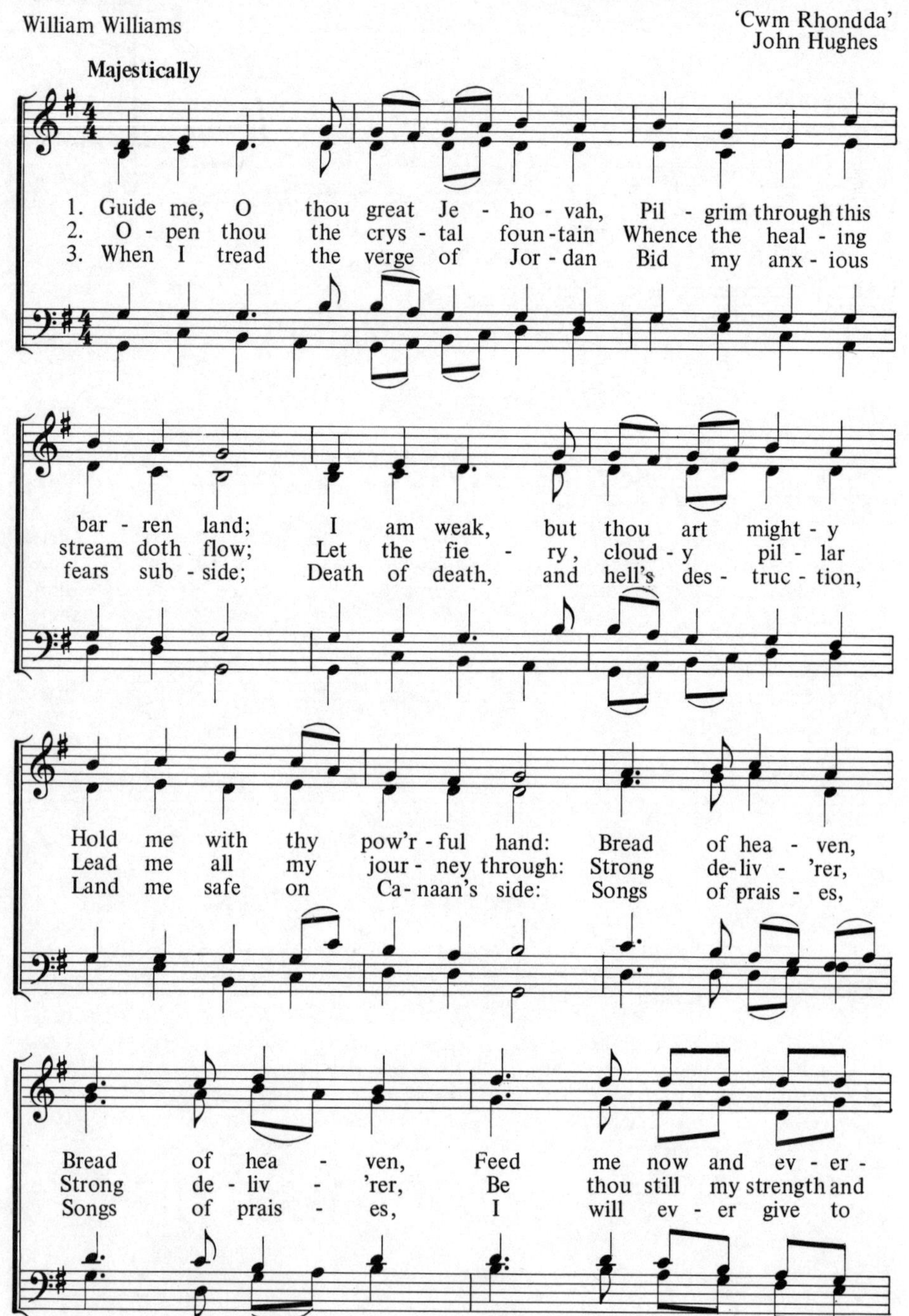
Majestically
1. Guide me, O thou great Je - ho - vah, Pil - grim through this
2. O - pen thou the crys - tal foun - tain Whence the heal - ing
3. When I tread the verge of Jor - dan Bid my anx - ious
bar - ren land; I am weak, but thou art might - y
stream doth flow; Let the fie - ry, cloud - y pil - lar
fears sub - side; Death of death, and hell's des - truc - tion,
Hold me with thy pow'r - ful hand: Bread of hea - ven,
Lead me all my jour - ney through: Strong de - liv - 'rer,
Land me safe on Ca - naan's side: Songs of prais - es,
Bread of hea - ven, Feed me now and ev - er -
Strong de - liv - 'rer, Be thou still my strength and
Songs of prais - es, I will ev - er give to

more, Feed me now_ and_ ev - er - more.
shield, Be thou still_ my_ strength and shield.
thee, I will ev - er_ give to thee.

66. God of grace and God of glory

Harry Emerson Fosdick

'Cwm Rhondda'
John Hughes

1. God of grace and God of glory,
On thy people pour thy power;
Crown thine ancient Church's story;
Bring her bud to glorious flower.
Grant us wisdom, grant us courage,
For the facing of this hour. *(repeat)*

2. Lo! the hosts of evil round us
Scorn thy Christ, assail his ways!
From the fears that long have bound us
Free our hearts to faith and praise:
Grant us wisdom, grant us courage,
For the living of these days. *(repeat)*

3. Cure thy children's warring madness,
Bend our pride to thy control;
Shame our wanton, selfish gladness,
Rich in things and poor in soul.
Grant us wisdom, grant us courage,
Lest we miss thy kingdom's goal. *(repeat)*

4. Set our feet on lofty places;
Gird our lives that they may be
Armored with all Christ-like graces
In the fight to set men free.
Grant us wisdom, grant us courage,
That we fail not man nor thee. *(repeat)*

67. God, make us your family

Capo 3 (A)
Tim Whipple
With pulsating rhythm
Refrain C (A)
Eb(C) F(D) C(A)
Your king - dom come, your will be done,
now that we have be - come your sons. Let the
r.h.
prayer of our hearts dail - y be: God,
make us your fam - - i - ly.
Fine
The
Fm(Dm) Cm(Am)
1. eyes of the blind shall be o - pen'd; the
2. ran - som'd of the Lord shall re - turn; the
3. na - tions will see their shame; the

Fm(Dm)
Cm(Am)
ears of the deaf shall hear. The
is-lands will sing his songs at last. The
one true God will be a - dored. They'll
Fm(Dm)
Cm(Am)
chains of the lame will be bro-ken;
chaff from the wheat shall be burned; his
turn from their for - tune and fame; his
Fm(Dm)
G(E)
D.C.
streams will flow in des-erts of fear.
D.C.
king-dom on earth, it shall come to pass.
ho - ly mountain shall be re - stored.
D.C.

Optional refrain for Christmastide:

Laude, Lauda, Laude, Lauda.
Gloria Emmanuel.
} *repeat.*

68. Once no people

Based on 1 Peter 2: 9-10
Maggie Durran

Betty Pulkingham

Bold, well-accented
Refrain
Am
Em
Am
For we are a cho - sen race, a roy - al priest-hood,
G
Am
G
last time
F Maj7
G
ho - ly na - tion. Once no peo-ple, now God's peo-ple, pro-
Am
G
A
claim - - - ing his mar - - - vel-lous light.
E

A9
A Maj7
Bm7
1. Sing the songs of faith - ful Zi - on,
2. Dance the steps of joy - ful Zi - on,
3. Taste the fruit of peace - ful val - leys,
4. We will serve through trib - u - la - - - tion,
A
Esus4
we are the stars and the grains of sand.
cym-bals harps and tam - bour-ines.
sip of the wine and eat the bread.
we will fol - low to the cross.
A9
A Maj7
Bm7
Through our faith we are made glo - - ri - ous;
Blow the trum - pet, sound the glo - - - ry
Know the shep - herd who is guid - - -ing,
Know the death and pain of suf - - fer-ing;

A
E sus4
we are sons of A - bra - ham.
in the pres - ence of the Lord.
the Lord, the Lamb of God.
God wipes the tears from our eyes.
8
E
D.C.
F Maj7
Now God's
light
D.C.
G
peo - ple
Am
G
pro - claim - - - - ing his mar - - - - vel-lous
A
light.
8

69. Comfort ye

Clint Taylor
Arr. Betty Pulkingham
Gently
Refrain
G C G
Com-fort ye, com-fort ye, my peo - ple.
D C G
Thus saith the Lord.
Fine
D C G D
1.Bear each oth - er up in your times of trou - ble strength-en your-
2. Love one an - oth - er as I have loved you, ev' - ry - thing
3. Bless the Lord for his great mer - cy, es- pe-cially for his
C G
selves in your times of peace.
else will fall in - to place.
Son Je - sus Christ.
D.C.

4. By my spirit you have great power
which enables you to do my work.

70. Wherever two or more

Smoothly and simply
Brian Howard
Refrain
E
B7
Wher - ev - er two or more are gath-ered in my name, there I am,
E
there I am; wher - ev - er two or more are gath-ered in my name,
B7
A B7
Fine
E
A
there I am in the midst of them
1. Be-hold what man-ner of
2.If we walk in the light_ as
E
B7
E
E7
love the Fa-ther gives that we should be called_ the sons of_ God. And
he is in the light,___ we___ shall al - ways_ live___ with him;
A
E
F♯
F♯7
B7
D.C.
now lit-tle child-ren, a - bide in the Lord; we shall all be like him.
for the_blood of___ Je - sus_Christ sets us free from sin.______

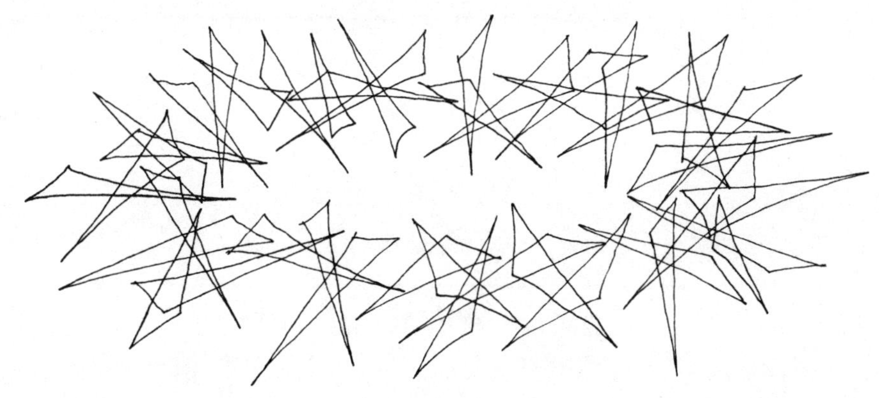

suffer-reign

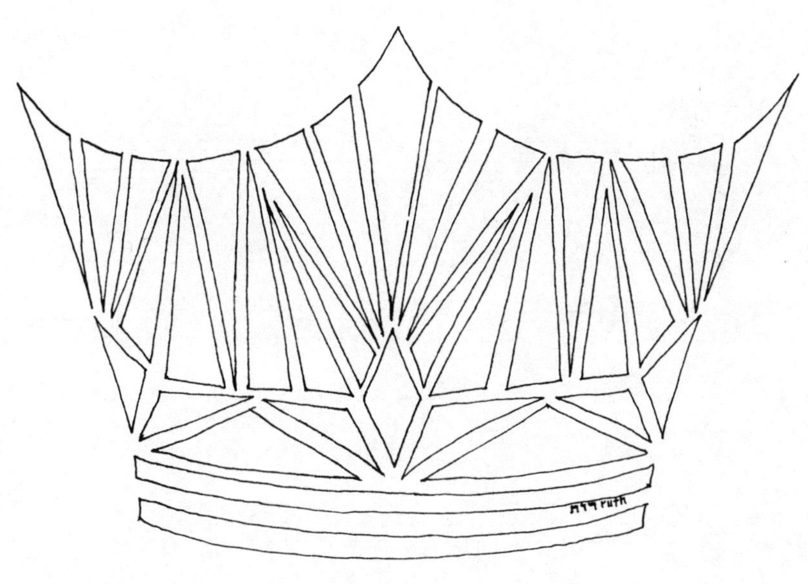

songs of faith and victory

71. In the name of Jesus

Anon.
Arr. Betty Pulkingham

Victoriously

E

In the name of Je - sus, in the name of Je - sus

B7
we have the vic - to - ry.

In the name of Je - sus, In the name of Je - sus

E
E7
de-mons will have to flee.
A
E
Who can tell what God can do?
B7
E
B7
E
E7
Who can tell of his love for you?
A
E
In the name of Je - sus, Je - sus,
A
B7
E
we have the vic - to - ry.

72. Fight the good fight

John S. B. Monsell

'Old Clarendonian'
Olwen Wonnacott

With vigour
1. Fight the good fight with all thy — might,
Christ is thy strength and Christ thy right;
Lay hold on life, and
it shall be thy joy — and crown e - ter - nal-ly.

72. Fight the good fight

John S. B. Monsell

1. Fight the good fight with all thy might,
   Christ is thy strength and Christ thy right;
   Lay hold on life, and it shall be
   Thy joy and crown eternally.

2. Run the straight race through God's good grace,
   Lift up thine eyes and seek his face;
   Life with its way before us lies,
   Christ is the path and Christ the prize.

3. Cast care aside, lean on thy Guide,
   His boundless mercy will provide;
   Trust, and thy trusting soul shall prove
   Christ is its life and Christ its love.

4. Faint not, nor fear, his arms are near;
   He changeth not, and thou art dear;
   Only believe, and thou shalt see
   That Christ is all in all to thee.

73. Jesus is a-drivin' out Satan

Capo 3 (Am)

Mary Ackroyd
Arr. Betty Pulkingham

Bold, blues feeling
Cm(Am)
Eb(C)
1. Je - sus is a-driv - in' out Sa - tan from
2. Je - sus is a might - y war - rior, he
3. He gives us his blood and bo - dy; in
4. You win the bat - tle for us,
F (D)
Cm(Am)
ev' - ry-where un - - der the sun.
teach - es us how to fight. 'Take my
his strength we must rest. We
we claim the pow - er you give.
Eb(C)
Je - sus is a-driv - in' out Sa - tan, you'd bet - ter
shield and my hel - met and my dou - ble edged sword.' Sa - tan
aren't the ones who fight the bat - tle when
We are your lov - in' peo - ple, and

F(D)
Cm(Am)
get up Sa - tan and run.
fades in the sight of the right.
Sa - tan puts us to the test.
by your word we will live.
Refrain
Cm(Am)
Eb(C)
Je - sus is the vic - tor, Je - - sus, God's son. Je-
F(D)
Cm(Am)
- sus is the king, the bat - tle is won.
Cm(Am)
Eb(C)
Je - sus is the vic - tor, Je - - sus, God's son. Je-
F(D)
Cm(Am)
- sus is the king, the bat - tle is won.

74. Faith is the victory

Refrain: John Yates
Verses: Betty Pulkingham

Refrain: Ira Sankey
Verses: Betty Pulkingham

With zest and buoyancy

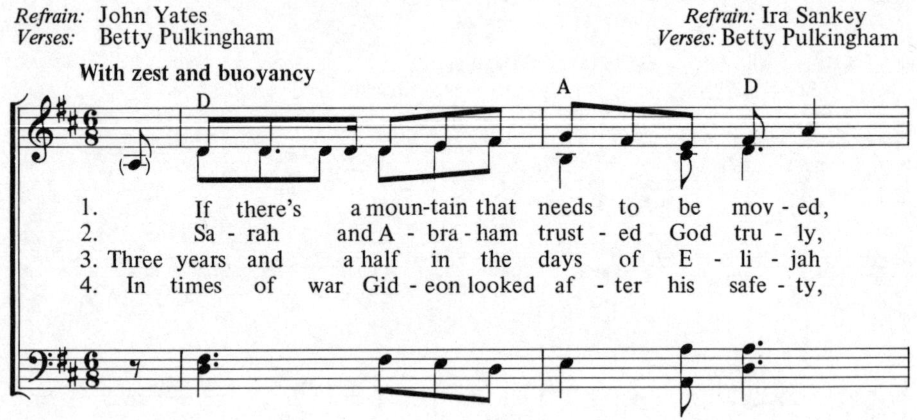
D
A
D
1. If there's a moun-tain that needs to be mov - ed,
2. Sa - rah and A - bra - ham trust - ed God tru - ly,
3. Three years and a half in the days of E - li - jah
4. In times of war Gid - eon looked af - ter his safe - ty,

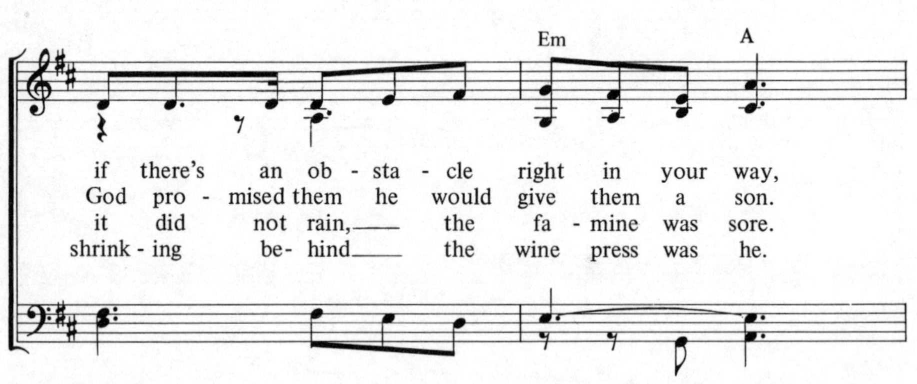
Em
A
if there's an ob - sta - cle right in your way,
God pro - mised them he would give them a son.
it did not rain, the fa - mine was sore.
shrink - ing be- hind the wine press was he.

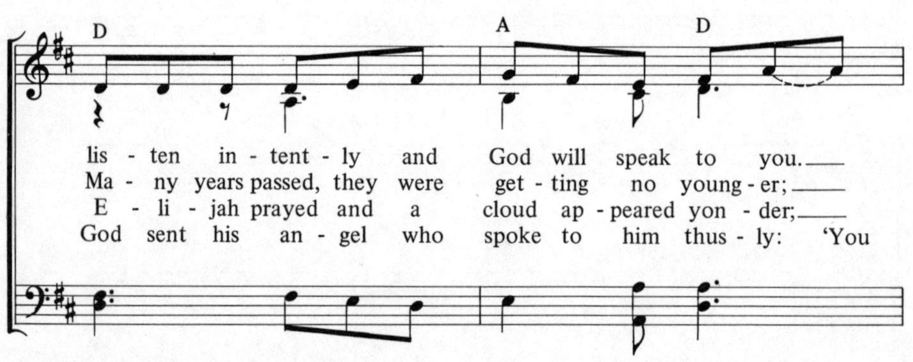
D
A
D
lis - ten in - tent - ly and God will speak to you.
Ma - ny years passed, they were get - ting no young - er;
E - li - jah prayed and a cloud ap - peared yon - der;
God sent his an - gel who spoke to him thus - ly: 'You

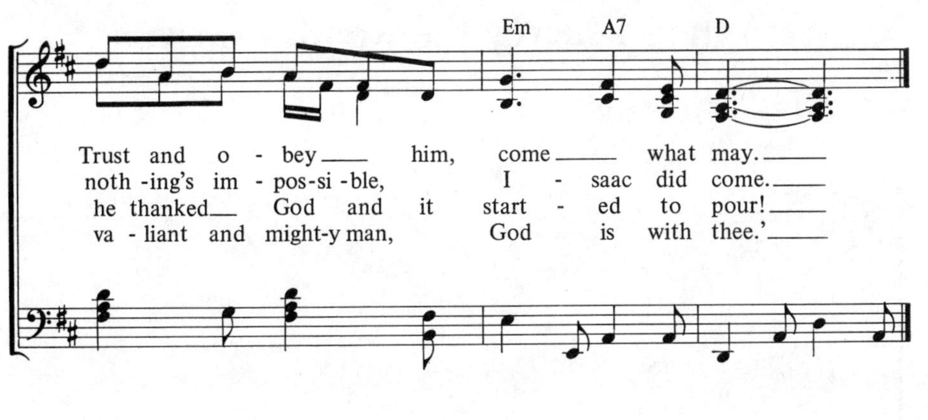
Em
A7
D
Trust and o - bey him, come what may.
noth -ing's im - pos-si - ble, I - saac did come.
he thanked God and it start - ed to pour!
va - liant and might-y man, God is with thee.'

Refrain
D
A
D
Faith is the vic - to-ry. Faith is the vic - to-ry.

G
D
A7
D
Oh, glo-ri - ous vic - to-ry that o - ver-comes the world.

75. When I survey the wondrous cross

Capo 4 (C)

Isaac Watts

Mikel Kennedy

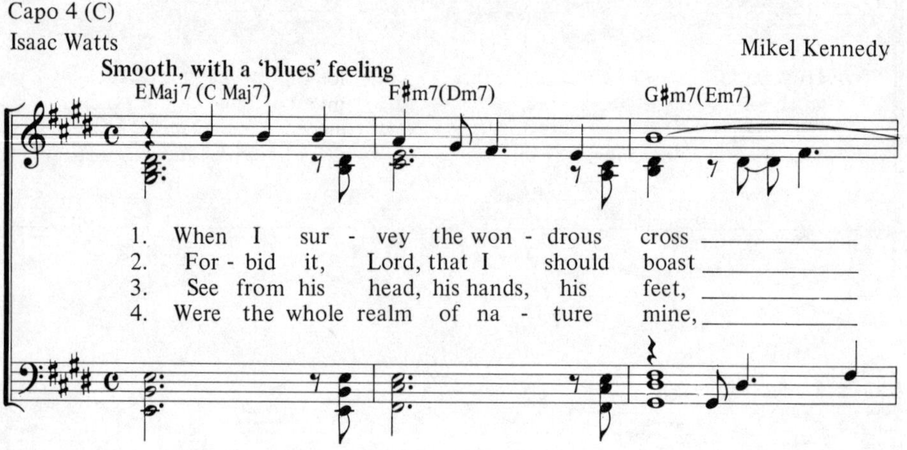
Smooth, with a 'blues' feeling
EMaj7 (C Maj7)
F♯m7(Dm7)
G♯m7(Em7)
1. When I sur - vey the won - drous cross
2. For - bid it, Lord, that I should boast
3. See from his head, his hands, his feet,
4. Were the whole realm of na - ture mine,

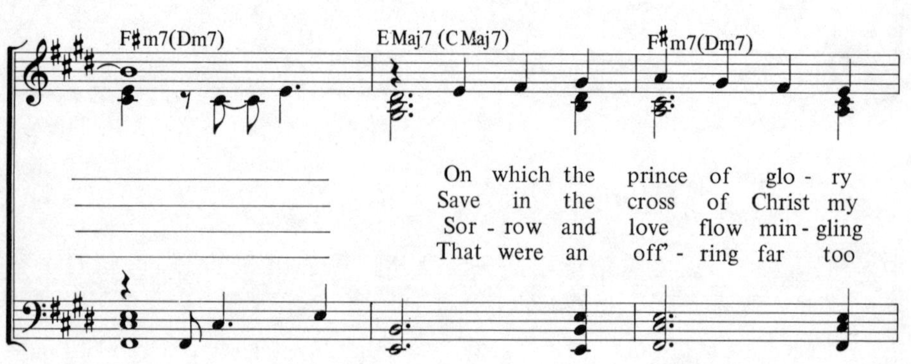
F♯m7(Dm7)
EMaj7 (C Maj7)
F♯m7(Dm7)
On which the prince of glo - ry
Save in the cross of Christ my
Sor - row and love flow min - gling
That were an off' - ring far too

G♯m7(Em7)
F♯m7(Dm7)
EMaj7 (C Maj7)
died, My rich - est
God; All the vain
down; Did e'er such
small; Love so a-

F♯m7(Dm7) G♯m7(Em7) F♯m7(Dm7)

gain ___ I count but loss, ___
things ___ that charm me most, ___
love ___ and sor - - row meet, ___
maz - - ing, so di - vine, ___

A(F) Am7(Fm7) E Maj7 (C Maj7)

And pour con - tempt on all my pride. ___
I sac - ri - fice them to his blood. ___
Or thorns com - pose so rich a crown? ___
De·mands my soul, my life, my all. ___

F♯m7(Dm7) G♯m7(Em7) F♯m7(Dm7)

1, 2, 3.

E Maj7 (C Maj7)
Final ending
Rit. and dim. ....

76. I am persuaded

Romans 8: 38-39

Joan Hettenhouser
Arr. Betty Pulkingham

Bold 'blues' rhythm
D
Bm
Em
A
For
D
Bm
Em
A
I am per-suad - ed that neith-er death, – nor life, nor
F♯m
G
A
an - gels nor prin - ci - pal - i - ties, nor
D
Bm
Em
A
powers, nor – things pre - sent, – nor an - y - thing – to come, nor

D
Bm
Em
A
height, nor depth, nor an - y oth - er crea- ture shall be
a - ble to sep - a - rate us from the love of God,
which is in Christ Je-sus our Lord.
r.h.
1.
2.
Praise God!

77. On Jordan's stormy banks

Samuel Stennett
Traditional
Arr. Betty Pulkingham
Wistful, not too slow
Em
Am
1. On— Jor - dan's storm - y banks I stand— and
2. When— shall I reach— that hap - py place— and
Em
B7
Em
cast a wish - ful eye to— Ca - naan's fair and
be for - ev - er blest? When— shall I— see my
B7
Em
hap - py land where my pos - ses - sions lie.
Fa - ther's face, and— in his— bo - som rest?
I am
Brightly, a little faster
E
B7
bound for the pro - mised land,— I am
E
B7
original tempo
Em
bound for the pro - mised land.
O— who will— come and

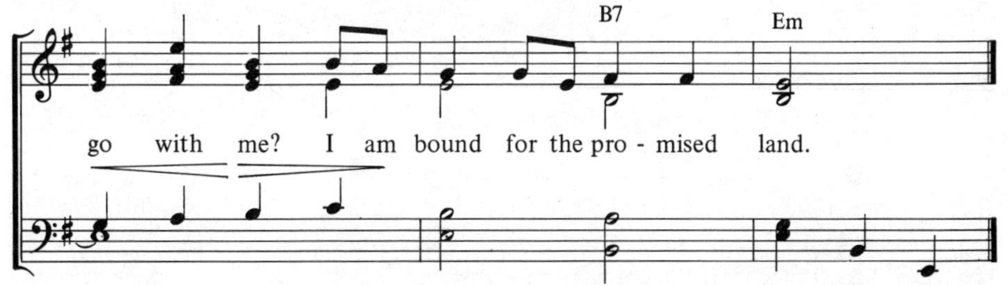
B7
Em
go with me? I am bound for the pro - mised land.

'On Jordan's stormy banks' and *'Come go with me to that land'* (the song that follows) create an unusual medley. Musically, they form a startling contrast; thematically, they make an interesting progression of thought.

78. Come go with me to that land

Traditional
Arr. Betty Pulkingham

Jauntily
E
E7
1. Well come go with me to that land, come go
lov - in' in that land, gon - na be
hon - ey in that land, milk and

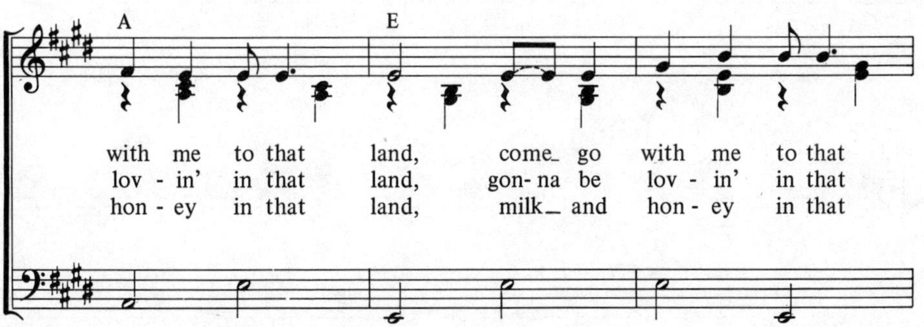
A
E
with me to that land, come go with me to that
lov - in' in that land, gon - na be lov - in' in that
hon - ey in that land, milk and hon - ey in that

F♯
B7
land where I'm bound. Come go
land where I'm bound. Gon-na be
land where I'm bound. Milk and
E
E7
A
with me to that land, come go with me to that
lov-in' in that land, gon-na be lov-in' in that
hon-ey in that land, milk and hon-ey in that
C
E
r.h.
land, to that land, to that
land, in that land, in that
land, in that land, in that
B7
E
A
Fine
E
land where I'm bound. 2. There's gon-na be
3. And milk and

Other verses may be added:

Gonna meet Jesus in that land .... Be singin' and dancin' in that land ....
Don't you know heaven is that land?..... *etc.*

79. He is my everything

Capo 1 (E)

Composer and author unknown
Arr. Betty Pulkingham

Worshipfully
F(E) B♭(A) C7(B7) F(E)
C7(B7)
He is my ev' - ry-thing, he is my all,
C7(B7)
Dm7 (C♯m7) C7(B7) F(E)
he is my ev' - ry- thing, both great and small.
B♭(A) C7(B7) F(E)
F7(E7)
B♭(A)
He gave his life for me, made ev'ry-thing new.
F(E)
C7(B7) F(E)
He is my ev' - ry- thing, he'll sat-is-fy you.

80. There's no greater name

Capo 1 (G)

Michael Baughen

With a good swing-fairly fast
A♭(G) Fm(Em) B♭m(Am) E♭7(D7)
1. There's no great - er name than Je - sus,
2. In our minds by faith pro fess - ing,
A♭(G) Fm(Em) B♭m(Am) E♭7(D7)
Name of him who came to save us,
In our hearts by in - ward bless - ing,
A♭(G) C7(B7) Fm(Em) A♭7(G7) D♭(C) 2nd. time E♭7(D7)
In that sav - ing name of Je - sus
On our tongues by words con-
A♭(G) E♭7(D7) A♭(G)
Ev' - ry knee should bow.

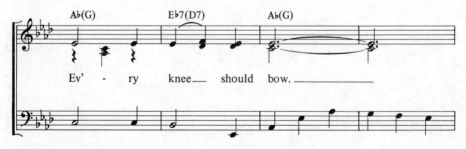

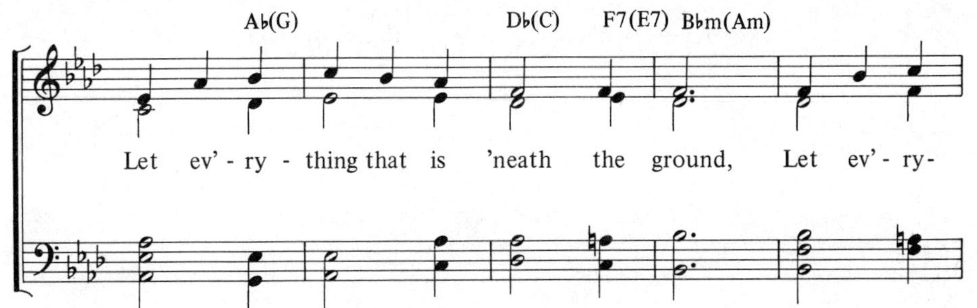
Ab(G)
Db(C)
F7(E7)
Bbm(Am)
Let ev' - ry - thing that is 'neath the ground, Let ev' - ry-

Eb(D)
Eb7(D7)
Ab(G)
thing in the world a - round, Let ev' - ry - thing that's

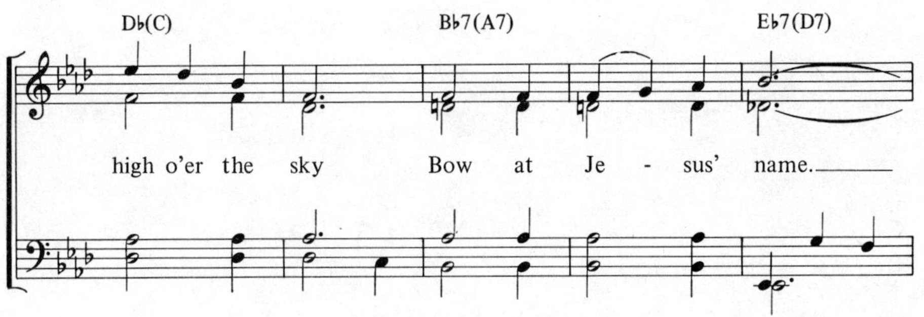
Db(C)
Bb7(A7)
Eb7(D7)
high o'er the sky Bow at Je - sus' name.

2nd. time
D.C.
Eb(D)
Ab(G)
fess - ing Je - sus Christ is Lord!

come as children

songs for children of all ages

SECTION 7

COME AS CHILDREN

SONGS FOR CHILDREN OF ALL AGES

81. I am so glad that Jesus loves me

Philipp Bliss
Arr. Betty Pulkingham

Happily
G
D7
G
1. I am so glad that our Fa - ther in heav'n
2. Though I for - get him and wan - der a - way;
3. O if there's on - ly one song I can sing,
D
G
(D7)
G
Tells of his love in the book he has given.
Still he doth love me wher - ev - er I stray.
When in his beau - ty I see the great King,
D7
G
Won - der - ful things in the Bi - ble I see;
Back to his dear lov - ing arms do I flee,
This shall my song in e - ter - ni - ty be,

C
D7
G
This is the dear - est, that Je - sus loves me.
When I re - mem - ber that Je - sus loves me.
O what a won - der that Je - sus loves me.

Refrain
C
I am so glad that Je - sus loves me,

D7
G
Je - sus loves me,
Je - sus loves me.
I am so glad that

C
D7
G
Je - sus loves me,
Je - sus loves e - ven me.

82. (Someone), Jesus loves you

Anon.
Arr. Betty Pulkingham

Simply
(Someone), Jesus loves you. (Someone), Jesus loves you. And love, love, love comes a-trickl'-in' down.
Seek and ye shall find, ask an-y-where, give a knock and the door shall be o-pen'd and
love, love, love comes a-trickl'-in' down.
last time, slowly
And love,
love, love comes a - trickl' - in' down.

83. Jesus loves Kristi*

(to Kristi)

Capo 1 (E)

Ann House

As a lullaby
F(E)
C7(B7)
Je - sus, Je-sus loves (name). Yes, he does, yes, he does.
F(E)
Je - sus, Je-sus loves (name). Yes, he does, yes, he does.
B♭(A)
B♭m(Am)
Je - sus, Je-sus loves (name). Yes, he does, yes, he does.
F(E)
C7(B7)
F(E)
B♭(A)
F(E)
And he wants (name) to love him too.

* In 1971 Kristi, age 4, went home to her heavenly Father. This song, composed by her mother shortly before her death, was a gift to Kristi, and now it belongs to the whole world.

84. On tiptoe

Capo 4 (C)
Verses: Maggie Durran
Refrain: Romans 8: 19
Philips Translation

Jodi Page
Arr. Betty Pulkingham

Gracefully

E(C)
B7(G7)
1. I
2. I
3. If
4. My
detached
E(C)
C♯m(Am)
F♯m(Dm)
B7(G7)
walk with you, my child-ren, through val - leys filled with gloom; in
made the mot-tled stickle-back to hide in cry - stal streams, the
life were filled with bub-bles, they'd glis - ten and they'd burst; if
love for you, my child-ren, puts rain-bows in your hand,
E(C)
C♯m(Am)
F♯m(Dm)
B7(G7)
ech - oes of the star - light and sha-dows of the moon. In the
star - ing owl to scan the night, the can-dle's gen - tle beams; I
life were filled with jew - els they'd line a rich man's purse; but
born of cloud-ed sor - rows in a sun-burst morn-ing land; they

E(C)
C♯m(Am)
F♯m(Dm)
B7(G7)
whisp-ers of the night-wind are gen - tle words for you to
made the sil - ly cam - el to roam the des - ert sand, but
life is filled with wa - ter that flows from depths of love, it
arch a - bove the smi - ling eyes where tears can still be seen, and a-
E(C)
C♯m(Am)
F♯m(Dm)
B7(G7)
touch you and as - sure you it's my world you're walk-in'
you I made, my child - ren, to walk and hold my
flows to fill your wear - i - ness with bless - - - ing from a-
dorn with gen - tle tremb-ling touch the bride who is my
E(C)
Refrain
C♯m(Am)
through.
hand.
bove.
own.
And all cre - a - tion's strain-ing on

F♯m(Dm) B7(G7) E(C) C♯m(Am)

tip-toe just to see___ the sons of God

F♯m(Dm) B7(G7) E(C) *last time.*

come_ in-to their own.

85. I sing a song of the saints of God

Lesbia Scott

'Grand Isle'
John Henry Hopkins

In sturdy march time

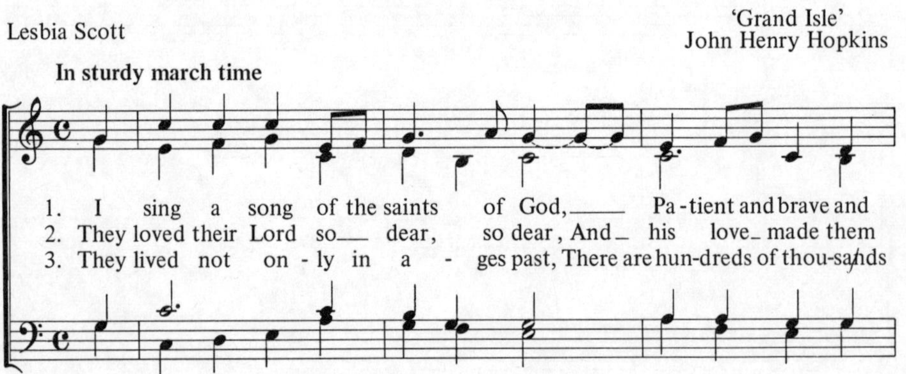
1. I sing a song of the saints of God,___ Pa-tient and brave and
2. They loved their Lord so_ dear, so dear, And_ his love_ made them
3. They lived not on-ly in a-ges past, There are hun-dreds of thou-sands

Used by permission of Morehouse-Barlow Co., New York.

true, Who toiled and fought and lived and died For the
strong; And they fol-lowed the right, for Je - sus' sake, The
still, The world is bright with the joy - ous saints Who
Lord they loved and knew. And one was a doc - tor, and
whole of their good lives long. And one was a sol - dier, and
love to do Je - sus' will. You can meet them in schools, or in
one was a queen, And one was a shep-herd-ess on the green: They were
one was a priest, And one was slain by a fierce wild beast: And there's
lanes or at sea, In church or in trains, or in shops or at tea, For the
all of them saints of God and I mean, God help-ing, to be one too.
not a - ny rea - son, no, not the least, Why I shouldn't be one too.
saints of God are just folk like me, And I mean to be one too.

86. Knock, knock

'Ask and it shall be given you'

Based on Luke 11: 9-13

Betty Pulkingham

Playfully
Refrain
D
G
D
Ask, and it shall be giv - en you. Seek, and ye shall
Knock on wood:
A
D
G
find. If you knock, knock, knock, the door will
D
A7
D
Fine
Verses
G
o-pen un-to you ev'-ry time.
1. If a son shall
2. If a son shall
3. If a son shall
D
G
D
ask his fa - ther for a piece of bread,
ask his fa - ther for a lit - tle fish,
ask his fa-ther for an egg o - ver light,

G D E7 A D.C.

will that fa - ther give his son a stone in - stead?
will that fa - ther give him a ser - pent in his dish?
will that fa - ther give him a scor-pi - on that can bite?

Verse 4.

Smoothly

G D G D

4. If ye then, be - ing e - vil, know how to give good things,

G D E7 A

How much more your lov - ing hea-ven-ly Fa - ther brings! Your

G D G D

lov - ing hea-ven-ly Fa - ther gives the best gift of all! He

G D E7 A D.C.

gives the Ho - ly Spi - rit un - to them that call on him.

87. Pullin' the weeds, Lord*

Max Dyer

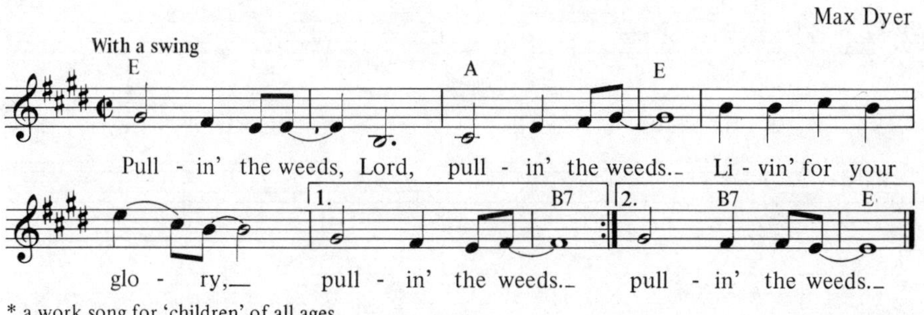

With a swing
E A E
Pull - in' the weeds, Lord, pull - in' the weeds. Li - vin' for your
1. B7 2. B7 E
glo - ry, pull - in' the weeds. pull - in' the weeds.

* a work song for 'children' of all ages.

Other suggested verses:

Sweepin' the floor, Lord.......
Goin' to school (church, bed, *etc!*), Lord.......
Singin' this song, Lord.......

88. One, two, three, Jesus loves me

Lisa Mazak
(age 9)

Happily
Refrain
E
A
E
A
E
One, two, three, Je-sus loves me. One, two,
B7
E
Fine
E
A
E
Je-sus loves you. 1. Three, four, he loves you more
A
E
B7
E
D.C.
E
than you've ev-er been loved be-fore. 2. Five, six, seven, we're
A
E
A
E
B7
E
D.C.
go-ing to heav'n. Eight, nine, it's tru-ly di-vine.
E
A
E
1. A
E
3. Nine, ten, it's time to end; but in-stead we'll
cresc.

B7 E D.C. 2. A E B7 E
sing it a - gain. there's no time to sing it a - gain.
rit. and dim.

89. Put on your boots

Sherrell Prebble

Western Americana

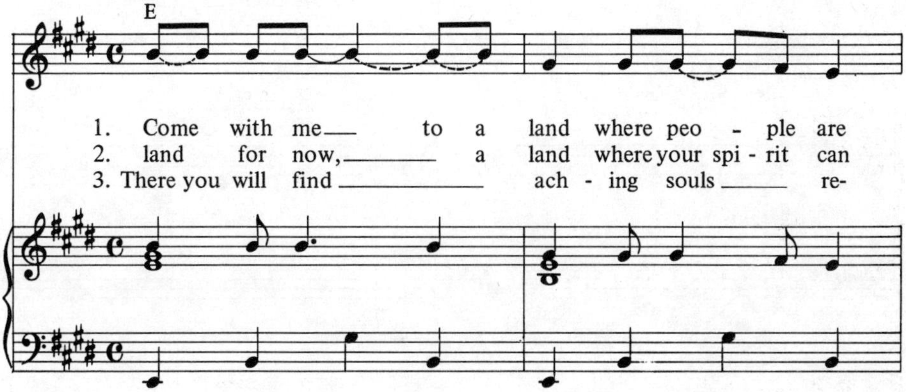

E

1. Come with me to a land where peo - ple are
2. land for now, a land where your spi - rit can
3. There you will find ach - ing souls re-

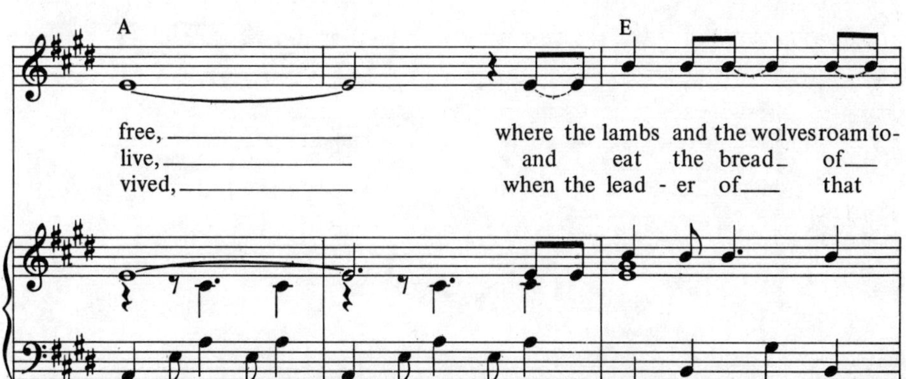

A E

free, where the lambs and the wolves roam to-
live, and eat the bread of
vived, when the lead - er of that

A
B7
geth - er through the coun - try. They
life that makes you whole.
land pass - es by. The
E
v. 2-3
say that a child can ride on a li - on's
When you're thirs - ty and you want a
lone - ly peo - ple find fel - - low-
A
E
back, and not one man steals
drink, they have liv - ing
ship, and there is plen - ty of

A
B7
E
Refrain
food _ from his bro - ther's shack. So
wa - ter for your souls.
heal - ing for the sick.
A
E
put on your boots, let's get on the road. There's
A
B7
1. E
just not that much time, you know.
2. E
D.C.
Final ending
know. 2. It's a

90. Jesus took my burdens

Anon.
Arr. Betty Pulkingham

Happily
E
1. Je-sus took my bur-dens and he rolled them in the sea,
2. Now I am hap-py, hap-py as can be,
B7
rolled them in the sea,
hap-py as can be,
E
rolled them in the sea.
hap-py as can be,
Je-sus took my bur-dens and he rolled them in the sea,
Now I am hap-py, hap-py as can be,
B7
nev-er to re-mem-ber an-y-more.
nev-er to re-mem-ber an-y-more.
E

'Jesus took my burdens' may be sung in sequence with the following song:

91. I must have Jesus

Anon.
Arr. Betty Pulkingham

Fast and light
E
1. I must have Je - sus in my whole life. I must have
B7
E
E7
Je - sus in my life. In my walk-ing, in my talk-ing, in my
A
Am
E
B7
E
sleep-ing, in my wak-ing, must have Je - sus in my life.

2. I have Christ Jesus in my whole life.
I have Christ Jesus in my life.
In my walking, in my talking,
In my sleeping, in my waking,
Have Christ Jesus in my life.

92. I'm not alone

Cheerfully

Diane Davis

Refrain
D
G
A7
I'm not a - lone for my Fa - ther is with me,
D
A7
with me wher-ev - er I go.
D
G
Gm
Speak-ing words of faith, of cour-age and of love, he's
Ped.
D
A7
last time
1-3. D
with me, he loves me wher - ev - er I go.
D
G
A7
1. Wak-ing in the morn - ing, get-ting read-y for school,
2. And when I find my - self in a mess,
3. All of my life ev'-ry - where that I go,

D
A7
D
walk-ing down the road,
in ___ class, at
I can trust in him,
call on his name and
I will walk with him,
prais-ing him and
G
Gm
D
A7
work, or at play,
watch him _ move,
bless - ing his name,
he's with me, he loves me wher - ev - er I
D
D.C. ⊕ D
go.
go.
he's
A7
with me, he loves me wher - ev - - - - - - - - - - - - - - - - - -
D
er I go.

93. Put on the whole armour of God

'The spiritual war'

Ephesians 6: 10-17

Shirley Lewis Brown

Martial

Refrain

A D A7

mf

Put on the whole ar - mour of

D
A
D
God, put on the whole ar-mour of God, put on the

A7
D
whole ar - mour of God, that you may

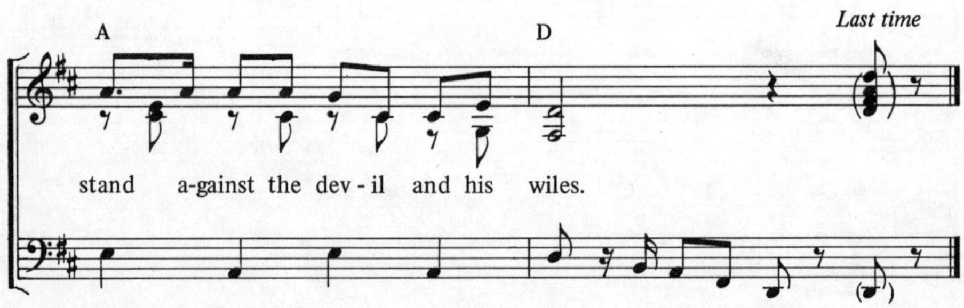

A
D
Last time
stand a-gainst the dev - il and his wiles.

A
E
1. Take your stand with truth as your belt.
2. Put on right-eous- ness for your breast - plate.
3. Shoe your feet with the gos - pel of peace.
4. As your hel - met don sal - va - tion from God.
5. In your hand take the sword of the Spi - rit,
6. A - bove all else take the shield of faith to

A
Take your stand with truth as your belt.
Put on right-eous - ness for your breast - plate.
Shoe your feet with the gos - pel of peace.
As your hel-met don sal - va - tion from God.
Which is real - ly the word of God.
quench all the fier - - - y darts of the wick - ed.

A7
D
Put on the whole ar- mour of

94. Clean hands

Capo 1 (E)

Author unknown

'Bethany'
Lowell Mason
Arr. Betty Pulkingham

Simply
F(E)
Bb(A)
F(E)
Clean hands or dirt - y hands, brown eyes or
C7(B7)
F(E)
Bb(A)
blue, pale cheeks or ro - sy cheeks,
F(E)
C7(B7)
F(E)
Bb(A)
Je - sus loves you. Come to him
F(E)
Bb(A)
F(E)
C7(B7)
while you may, be his lit - tle lambs to - day.
F(E)
Bb(A)
F(E)
C7(B7)
F(E)
Clean hands or dirt - y hands, Je - sus loves you.

95. Bless you, Jesus

Robert Reynolds

Playfully
E
B7
Bless you, Je - sus, bless you. Bless you, Je - sus,
E
bless you. Bless you, Je - sus, bless you.
B7
E
All the peo-ple now, bless you.

Other verses may be added:

Love you.......... Trust you....... Serve you....... Praise you.......

Last verse:

Amen, Jesus, Amen. *(repeat twice).*
All the people now say, 'Amen.'
(spoken)

96. He's my rock, my sword, my shield

Author unknown
Verse 2: Wendy Rhodes

Composer unknown
Arr. Jeanne Harper

With abandon
D A D D7
1. He's my rock, my sword, my shield, He's the
2. He's my peace, my joy, my love, My name's
G D
wheel in the mid-dle of the wheel; He's the li - ly of the val - ley, the
written in his book a - bove, He's the cap-tain of my company in the
E7 A A7 D D7
bright and morn-ing star. Makes no differ - ence what you say, I'm go-ing
bat - tle of the Lord. Makes no difference what the devil may do, I've got
G D A7
on my knees and pray, I'm gon-na see my Lord in glo - ry one of these
vic-try, how a-bout you? I'm gon-na see my Lord in glo - ry one of these

Refrain
D
D7
G
days.
days.
I'm gon-na see my Lord in glo - ry one of these
D
G
D
G
days.
He's the rock of my soul and I'm gon-na sing his
A7
D
D7
praise. (Hal - le - lu - jah) He's my rock, my sword, my shield, He's the
G
D
wheel in the mid - dle of the wheel. I'm gon - na
A7
D
see my Lord in glo - ry one of these days.

go forth!

songs of outreach

97. Prayer of St. Francis

Sebastian Temple
Arr. Betty Pulkingham

Flowing
D
1. Make me a chan-nel of your peace. Where
2. Make me a chan-nel of your peace. Where
3. Make me a chan-nel of your peace. It
Em
A7
there is hat-red let me bring your love; where
there's des-pair in life let me bring hope; where
is in par-don-ing that we are par-doned, in
Em
there is in-jur-y, your par-don, Lord; and
there is dark-ness, on-ly light; and
giv-ing to all men that we re-ceive; and in

Em7
A7
D
Fine
D7
*
where there's doubt, true faith in you.
where there's sad - ness, ev - er joy.
dy - ing that we're born to e - ter - nal life.
Oh,
G
D
mas - ter, grant that I may nev - er seek
so
A7
D
D7
much to be con - soled as to con - sole;
to be
G
D
un - der - stood as to un - der - stand;
to be
E
E7
A
D.C.
loved, as to love with all my soul.

* Voices may sing in two-part harmony.

98. The light of Christ

Donald Fishel
Arr. Betty Pulkingham

Flowing
Refrain
C
Part 1. The light of Christ has
Part 2. The light of Christ
F
Dm
G
C
come in - to the world, the light of
has come in - to the world, the
C
F
G
1-3
Christ has come in - to the world.
light of Christ has come.

Verses
F C F G
1. All men must be born a-gain to see the king-dom of
2. God gave up his on-ly Son out of love for the
3. The light of God has come to us so that we might have sal-
C F G C
God; the wa-ter and the Spi-rit bring new
world, so that all men who be-lieve in him will
va-tion; from the dark-ness of our sins we walk in-to
Dm G C
D.C. 4.
life in God's love.
live for ev-er. world.
glo-ry with Christ Je-sus.
D.C.

99. Drop everything and go

Diane Davis

Lightly
Refrain
D
G
D
It makes no dif - fer-ence who you__ are. ________ It
A7
D
makes no dif - fer-ence where you're go - ing to; ________
G
D
when Je - sus calls to___ you,
A
D
A7
D
Fine
drop ev'ry-thing and go, ________ drop ev'ry-thing and go.

D G D A A7
1. Pe - ter was a fish - er - man, he was fish-ing in his
2. Laz' - rus was dead and bound, dead and bound in his
3. Je - sus is the Son of God, his Fa - ther called un - to
D G
boat. When Je - sus called to
grave. When Je - sus called to
him, said, 'My peo - ple need to be re-
D A D
him, he dropped ev'- ry - thing and he went, he
him, he dropped all his bonds and he went, he
deemed.' He took up his cross and he went to
A7 D D.C.
dropped ev'- ry - thing and he went.
dropped all his bonds and he went.
die for you and me.
D.C.

100. Let there be peace on earth

Sy Miller and Jill Jackson
Slowly
C Am Dm7 G7 C F
Let there be peace on earth and let it be-
Let peace be - gin with me, let this be the
C Dm G7 C B7
gin with me; Let there be peace on
mo - ment now. With ev' - ry step I
Em G7 2nd. time
earth, the peace that was meant to be, With
take, let this be my sol - emn vow: To
Am Em F G7
God as our Fa - ther, bro - thers all are

C
Am7
D7
G
we, ___ Let me walk with my bro - ther ___
Am7
D7
G
G7
___ in per - fect har - mo ny. ___
C
C aug.
F
take each mo-ment and live each mo-ment in peace e-
D7
C
E7
F
ter - nal - ly. ___ Let there be peace on
C
F
Dm7
G7
C
earth and let it be - gin with me. ___

101. Freely, freely

Carol Owens

Smoothly
E
C♯m
F♯m7
1. God for - gave my sin in Je - sus'
pow'r is giv'n in Je - sus'
B7
F♯m7
B7
name. I've been born a - gain in
name. In earth and heav'n in
E Maj7
E7
A
Je - sus' name. And in Je - sus'
Je - sus' name. And in Je - sus'
E
A
B7
E
name I come to you to
name I come to you to

G#m F#m7 B7 E B7

slowly

share his love as he told me to.
share his pow'r as he told me to. } He said

Refrain *a tempo*

E F#m7 B7

free - ly, free - ly you have re - ceived;

E

free - ly, free - ly give.

F#m7 B7

Go in my name and be - cause you be - lieve,

E 1. 2.

oth - ers will know that I live. 2. All

* For variation, some voices may sing in thirds above the refrain melody, like this:

etc.

102. The Spirit is a-movin'

Carey Landry

Quick tempo, but steady
E
A
E
The Spi-rit is a-mov-in' all o-ver, all

D
E
Fine
o-ver this land.
4. The
r.h.

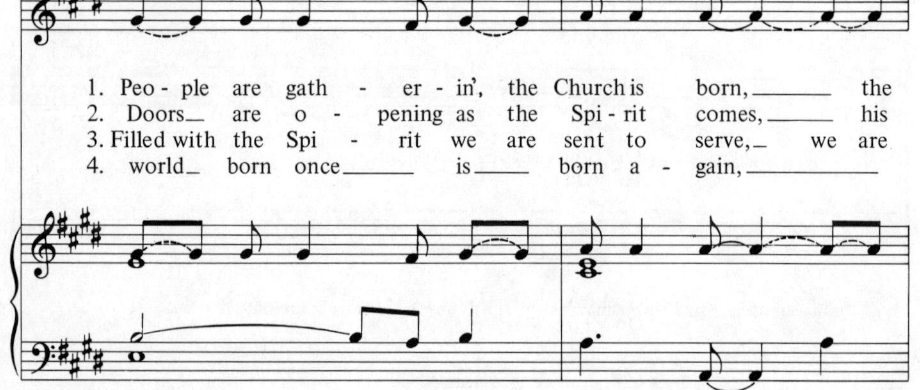
E
A
1. Peo-ple are gath-er-in', the Church is born, the
2. Doors are o-pening as the Spi-rit comes, his
3. Filled with the Spi-rit we are sent to serve, we are
4. world born once is born a-gain,

E
D
Spi - rit is a - blow - in' on a world re-
fire is burn - ing in his peo - - - - - - ple
called out as bro - thers, we are called to
we re - cre - ate it in love and

E
born.
now.
work.
joy.
The
r.h.

5. Old men are dreaming dreams,
And young men see the light.

6. Old Walls are falling down,
And men are speaking with each other.

7. The Spirit fills us with his power
To be his witnesses to all we meet.

8. The Spirit urges us to travel light
To be men of courage who spread his fire.

9. God has poured out his Spirit
On all, on all of mankind.

103. Moto Imeaka

Capo 1 (E)

East African folk song
Arr. Betty Pulkingham

Full and free
F(E)
(Refrain) Mo - - - - - - to im - ea - ka le - o,
(1.) fire is burn - ing in my soul, God's
C(B)
Mo - - - - - - to ni - ka - zi ya Ye - su,
fire is mak - ing me whole, God's
F(E)
B♭(A)
Mo - - - - - - to im - ea - ka le - o, Tu
fire is sweep - ing o'er the earth. Praise
With rhythmic precision and drive
C(B)
C7(B7)
F(E)
im - be Hal - le - lu - jah, Mo - to im - ea - ka, Tu
God, I've got God's fire and it's burn - ing in my soul, Praise

C(B)
C7(B7)
F(E)
Fine
im - be Hal - le - lu - jah, Mo - to im - ea - ka.
1. God's
God. I've got God's fire and it's burn-ing in my soul.
(Refrain)

*This song in Swahili is sung throughout East Africa. The literal English translation of the refrain is: 'The fire is burning today, fire is the work of Jesus, the fire is burning today, let us sing Hallelujah, the fire is burning.' The English verse in the musical text has essentially the same meaning. Other suggested verses: 'God's Spirit is burning.....','God's power is burning.....'. The last line may be repeated accumulatively, in reverse order: 'Praise God I've got God's Spirit.....', 'power.....', 'fire.'

104. And ye shall have power

Acts 1: 6-8

Clive Corrin
Arr. Betty Pulkingham

With a lilt

A Bm
When Je - sus met with his dis - ci - ples,

E7 A
when they'd all come to - geth - er, they

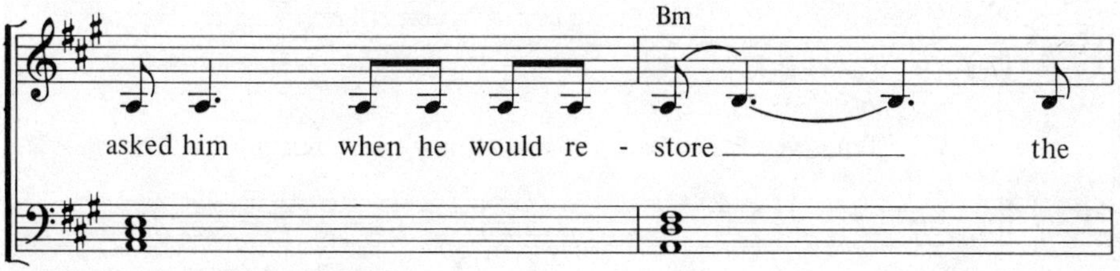

Bm
asked him when he would re - store the

E7
A
king - dom of Is - rael.
D
He told them that the time was
C#m
not for them to know, the
D
A
times and the sea - sons were his Fa - ther's,
E7
on - ly he would know.
* A
D
'But ye shall have pow'r

E7
A
when the Spi - rit comes on you.
D
Ye shall be my wit - ness - es
E7
A
to the ends of the earth;
Bm
to all Je - ru - sa - lem,
E7
A
through all Ju - de - a,
Bm
and in Sa - ma - ri - a,

E7
A
to the ends of the earth.
E7
A
to the ends of the earth.'

105. Come to the waters

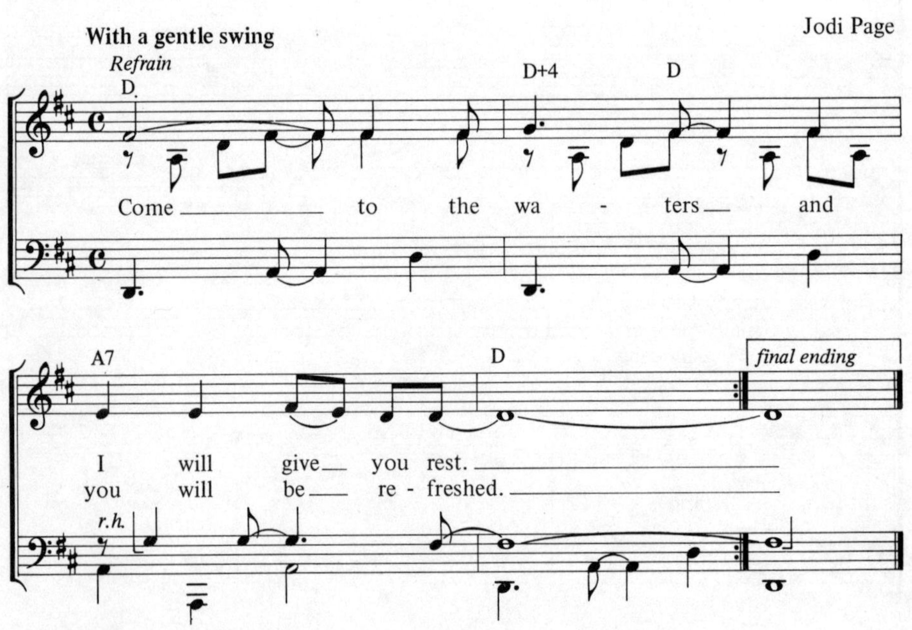
With a gentle swing
Jodi Page
Refrain
D.
D+4
D
Come to the wa - ters and
A7
D
final ending
I will give you rest.
you will be re - freshed.
r.h.

D
A7
D
1. Je - sus said, 'Come un - to
2. Je - sus said of the wa - ters
3. Je - sus said, 'He who be-
4. So with joy ye shall draw
A7
G
A
me all ye wea - - - - - - - - -
that he gave, he who drinks
lieves in me out of him shall
wa - ter out of wells
D
D.C.
- - - ry, hea - vy la - den.'
shall nev - er thirst a - gain.
flow liv - ing wa - ters.'
of sal - va - tion.
D.C.

106. Jesus! the name high over all

Charles Wesley

'Lydia'
Thomas Phillips

With strength

1. Je - sus! the name high o - ver all,
2. Je - sus! the name to sin - ners dear,
3. Je - sus! the pris - 'ners' fet - ters breaks,

In hell or earth, or sky; An - gels and
The name to sin - ners giv'n; It scat - ters
And brui - ses Sa - tan's head; Pow'r in - to

men be - fore it fall, And de - vils fear and
all their guil - ty fear, It turns their hell to
strength-less souls it speaks, And life in - to the

fly, And de - vils fear and fly.
heav'n, It turns their hell to heav'n.
dead, And life in - to the dead.

4. O that the world might taste and see
  The riches of his grace;
The arms of love that compass me
  Would all mankind embrace. *(repeat)*

5. His only righteousness I show,
  His saving grace proclaim;
'Tis all my business here below
  To cry: 'Behold the lamb!' *(repeat)*

6. Happy, if with my latest breath
  I might but gasp his name;
Preach him to all, and cry in death;
  'Behold, behold the lamb!' *(repeat)*

107. The Spirit of the Lord

Isaiah 61: 1-2
Jim Strathdee
A relaxed and easy tempo
G Em C D *
The Spi - rit of the Lord is up - on me, be -
G Em C D *
cause he has a - noint - ed me to
G Em C D *
preach good news to the poor. He has
G Em C D *
sent me to pro-claim re - lease to the cap - tives and re-
G Em C D *
cov-er-ing of sight to the blind,
G Em C D *
to set at lib-er-ty those who are op-press-ed, to pro-
G Em C D G *
claim the ac-cept - a - ble year of the Lord.

May be sung without accompaniment, antiphonally: the leader sings a phrase, the people repeat it, and this pattern continues throughout the seven musical phrases of the song (marked*). Then all sing the song without the repeats.

108. Come follow me now

Capo 1 (E)

Anna Withey
(age 10)

Simple and unhurried

F(E) C7(B7)

Come fol-low me now, come fol-low me now, come fol-low me

last time ⊕ B♭(A)

now, said Je - sus. 1. He died on the cross__ and__
2. I share my bo - dy with the

F(E) C7(B7) F(E)

bore all our pain. I__ walk in his love, and__ he sends the
whole of the world; if you drink of my blood, you will live ev - er-

B♭(A) F(E)

rain to wa - ter the plants that he gives to us. And
more. So fol - low me now, go tell the good news that

C7(B7) F(E) F(E) ⊕ *last time*

I do know he loves us.
Christ is liv - ing in us. Come Je - - sus.

Index

Topical Index

GROWTH AND MATURITY
(see Wholeness)

HEALING (see Wholeness)

HOLY COMMUNION
(see Kingdom, Liturgical songs)

HOPE AND VISION

KINGDOM

LITURGICAL SONGS

Introit

Doxology

Psalms

SEASONAL SONGS

Advent

Christmas

Epiphany

Passiontide

Easter

Ascension

Pentecost

Choirmaster's Guide

The following are appropriate for *CHOIRS:*

UNISON SONGS

As a doe 101 SOLW
God and man at table 67 SOLW
Hail to the Lord's anointed 2 FS
How sweet the name 48 SOLW
I heard the voice of Jesus say 49 FS
I love the name of Jesus 21 FS
Jesus, Lamb of God 41 FS
Let your light shine 122 SOLW
My song is love unknown 20 FS
O give thanks unto the Lord (Psalm 136) 38 FS
On Jordan's stormy banks 77 FS
Praise my God with the tambourine 7 FS
The shepherd of my soul 18 FS
Song of Simeon 39 FS
This is the feast 59 FS
Triumphant Zion 63 FS
We will sing to the Lord our God 13 FS
Who are my mother and my brothers? 62 FS

TWO-PART SONGS

And ye shall have power 104 FS
Freely, freely 101 FS
He shall teach you all things 41 FS
I will arise 33 FS
The light of Christ 98 FS
Prayer of St. Francis 97 FS
Sing praise to the Lord forever (Jacob's Song) 10 FS

ROUNDS

Father, we adore you 26 SOLW
God is working his purpose out 92 SOLW
Jesus, Jesus 17 FS
The Lord is my shepherd 108 SOLW
Rejoice in the Lord always 10 SOLW
Seek ye first 58 SOLW
Tallis' Canon 43 FS

SONGS AND HYMNS IN FOUR-PART HARMONY
(descants indicated by *.)

The following songs have verses which may be sung as *SOLOS* or by *SOLO ENSEMBLES:*

Index of Titles and First Lines

The first line of a song is included, in italic type, only where it differs from the title. SOLW – *Sound of Living Waters.* FS – *Fresh Sounds.*